Folk Tales of Ayrshire

Tony Bonning
Illustrations by Jo Jackson Bonning

First Published in Great Britain, 2021.

ISBN – 978 1 911043 12 6

Published by Carn Publishing Ltd.,
Lochnoran House,
Auchinleck,
Ayrshire, KA18 3JW.

www.carnpublishing.com

Printed by Bell & Bain Ltd.,
Glasgow, G46 7UQ.

TONY BONNING

Tony Bonning was born into a Scots-speaking, Carrick farming family in 1948. He has written several best-selling books and is a noted storyteller and musician. In his persona as Aiken Drum he has performed thousands of shows for children. Tony is the founder of the Galloway Children's Festival, the Play-it-by-Ear music groups and co-founder of the poetry magazine, Markings. In 2002 he was part of the group that established the popular Wickerman Festival. He enjoys nothing more than hillwalking with his wife, Jo Jackson-Bonning, illustrator of this book, and writing poetry.

JO JACKSON-BONNING

Jo Jackson-Bonning trained as a textile designer studying in Derby and Goldsmith's, London. She moved with her son to Galloway in 1999 and taught drama in secondary schools in the region for eighteen years. Illustrating the tales has meant a lot to Jo, as it is her second collaboration with writer Tony Bonning, an Ayrshire lad; as is her father, who was also born and raised in Ayrshire.

Dedication

For my firstest bestest friend Hunter (McQuater)
And for Ken and Mary Jackson for their wonderful tales
Tony Bonning

To the dear memory of, and to the deep love of
Charles and Barbara Bonning, Ayrshire sweethearts
Jo Jackson-Bonning

Contents

Illustrations

Introduction

The word Folklore was coined by Professor William John Thoms in 1846 to replace the unwieldy *popular antiquities*. The word means *people learning* and includes the culture, manners, customs, traditions and beliefs of a people. Folk Tales and Fairy Tales, while a part of folklore, are often viewed as a separate field of study and learning – a storyteller isn't always a folklorist nor a folklorist a storyteller, though each will, undoubtedly, be interested in the other.

But who listens to fairy tales nowadays? It's all computer games for children. Or is it?

I was fortunate to be born in Carrick into what was the last, truly Scots-speaking generation. We were a people of the land and our roots lay in farming where the old language was still prevalent. Like others of my generation, an attempt was made, sometimes literally, to thrash it out of us. Too late. Like the Jesuit maxim, 'Give me a child for the first seven years and I will give you the man,' we were too well indoctrinated; thankfully. We *hirpled up the braes, louped dykes an guddled troot*. Dinnertime was twelve midday and we ate it in silence. We had equality, for everyone worked, and hard. I've crawled along *dreels o tumshies*, thinning by hand beside my mother and father, although dad would sometimes use the hoe to save his back. My maternal grandfather owned and hauled threshing mills, using a steam traction engine, and I would help where I could, usually handing the next bag as the last filled with grain. All the workers, and there were many at the hairst (harvest), spoke the thick language of the South-West: earthy and tactile; little different from the poetry of Burns, which we understood, with few references to the glossary. I was doubly fortunate, for my mother was full of tales, poems and songs. Many about past life and culture: everyone thinks that Ailsa Craig is something called a 'volcanic plug'. What kind of nonsense is that to tell anyone? It was because of a fight between an Irish giant and a Scots giant. 'They wur flingin muckle stanes at yin anither, an yin landit juist aff o Girvan.' That's a much better story. I still found out what a volcanic plug was in case she was 'juist kiddin'.

Many of the tales in this book are hidden away in old, little-seen volumes and were effectively lost to the present. It is with great thanks to Dane Love and Carn Publishing for allowing me the privilege of recovering, collecting, saving and writing them for a modern audience.

So, who listens to fairy tales nowadays? Well, I travel the country, along with many other practitioners of the art, and tell tales to hundreds, even thousands of children and adults every year. As they say, the news of the demise of storytelling is a little premature.

This book is in honour of those past generations who laid the foundations of our world and created these tales.

Hamesang

The whirlin, skirlin, tirlin trill
O the lang-nebbit whaup upo the hill;
Its curlew caa, the rise an faa
As it circles ower baith muir an shaw.
It maks ma heart sae dowf an sair,
Fer it reminds me evermair,
O hame an folk an kith an kin
That lie aneath its halloed grun.

Tony Bonning

Note: While the narrative of the tales is in English, most of the dialogue is in Scots. In the language of the fifteenth, sixteenth and seventeenth centuries, Scots speakers tended to stress the ending of a verb in *it* rather than *ed*. Best known in the Selkirk Grace: *An sae the Lord be thankit*. The *ing* ending in verbs belongs to South-East England and is not used in many, if any, other English regional dialect or Scots, where it ends in *in*. There are words in the text that are difficult or unusual, so a glossary is provided at the rear or occasionally alongside, as in the poems. If you read the Scots aloud, you can often get the gist.

Speaking in Scots is neither wrong nor bad nor slang. The Scots Makars of the sixteenth century were the most celebrated poets in Europe and Burns has a world-wide appeal – Abraham Lincoln, president of the United States, had a copy of his poems on his bedside table and could recite the whole of *Tam o Shanter* in Scots: shames us, rather. That there was a concerted Westminster Government effort, in collusion with the Education Department of the Scottish Office, to eradicate Scots and Gaelic is nothing less than racist and supercilious arrogance. Lose the language and we risk losing a large part of our unique culture.

1
A Bit of What You Fancy

In the time of Robert Burns, great sailing vessels plied the oceans in search of sugar and spice and all things nice. They came to Ayr from all points of the compass and laid out their treasures on the wood and stone quay. Here the merchants of the town paid out their pound Scots and took away the wares to sell. Among the traders were itinerant packmen who paid their punds, shillins and bawbees, loaded up their Gypsy Cob ponies and headed into the uplands of Kyle and Carrick, visiting the fermtouns, cottars and hill shepherds. Packmen were easily identifiable with their weather-beaten faces, stout blue coats, corduroy breeks and swandown waistcoats. Below they wore woollen stockings and strong well-made boots reinforced with hobnails; and for protection, thigh length gaiters called cootikens. As well as the horses, they would be accompanied by one or two pack-laden dogs and on their own back, a large bale of goods. In his hand a packman always carried a walking stick; apart from helping him negotiate the trackways, it could also be used, when having a momentary break, to prop up the pack.

One such packman had wound his way up the River Doon by way of Dalrymple and Dalmellington. His plotted track was up to the headwaters of the Doon over to Carsphairn then down the River Ken to Kirkcudbright to reload at the harbour and return to Ayr by another route. As he headed into the fastness of the mountains towards a shepherd's cot up the Gala Lane beyond Loch Doon, storm clouds appeared away to the south-west. It was now after sunset, darkness threatened, and a wind was rising. He let the pony lead, the beast knowing every hummock, moss hag and peatbog on their way. He walked in the lee of the beast, his head bowed, one hand holding on his 'guid blue bonnet' as the wind snatched at it; the two lurcher dogs kept in close to his heels. They arrived at the shepherd's butt and ben in the pitch dark. The horse instinctively went to the butt door and the packman followed. He removed his flintlock pistol from a leather bag on the horse's neck and entered the room, then felt in his pocket and withdrew a waxed cloth. From this he removed a small square of charcloth, stuck it in the firing pan and pulled the trigger. He blew on it until it glowed red hot than fired up some dry moss he also kept in the waxed rag. In the glow of the smouldering moss he found a taper on a shelf, lit it then lit the storm lamp beside it. The space glowed bright and revealed a cow lying on a bed of heather and two collie dogs. The packman guided the pony in and then called in his dogs. The collies growled but he shushed them. He unloaded the packs from the pony including two small kegs, one of whisky one of strong beer. He left the blanket on to allow the beast to cool slowly, then he unloaded the dogs. From the packs he withdrew two wooden bowls, a head-bag for the horse and a small sack of grain. He poured some into the bag and placed it over the pony's head, then some into each dish for the dogs. Next, he lifted the small keg of beer and made for the ben of the house. As he came around the gable into the face of the wind, he could hear a banging noise from nearby, but could not see the cause in the dark. He reached the front door and hammered hard. The door was opened by a handsome woman, 'Cam awa in Sanny afore get blawit tae Hell an back.' The packman entered, put his back to the door and pushed it closed then stood for a moment, glad to be in the warmth of the room. 'Thanks, Nel,' he said, setting down the barrel. He looked over to the shepherd, who was sitting in the inglenook, smoking his clay pipe 'Evenin Andrew.'

'Evenin Sanny, I see ye made it.'

'Aye, but it's turnin intae a wild nicht.' He looked about the lamplit room and over to the chest where a baby lay sleeping in the bottom drawer, then around the room, his eyes settling on a large cake cooling on the windowsill, 'My that's a gran smell,' he said.

'Aye. A've juist makit a Dundee cake. Wuid ye like a piece?' said Helen.

'Aye, no hauf.'

The shepherd sat upright, 'Haud on a meenit. The cake's nae coolt yet; gin ye cut it, it'll faa apairt. He can hae a bit the morn's mornin.'

'The man's hungert Andy, a'll gie him a piece the nou.'

'A've said ma bit,' said the shepherd, with finality.

'It's fine,' said the packman, 'It'll taste better in the mornin. Noo, wha's fer a wee cog o beer?'

The atmosphere settled and beer was passed along with oatcakes and kebbuck. 'A hear a bangin noise fae the kailyaird. Whit is it?' said Sanny.

'Ach, it's a piece o that new-fanglt corrugaited airn that I pit on the roof o the wee hoose. A shuid hae pit another nail in it, bit A ran oot. A wis hopin ye haed a pickle.'

'A think a hae somethin that micht dae the job. Wull a get them?'

'Naw! I'll get them in the mornin. As lang as the win disnae get ony worse.'

The packman passed on news from Ayr and from the fermtouns along the way, ensuring he was discreet in what he said. After a few cogs, more old stories appeared: how the minister at Carsphairn confounded the Devil and how the farmer at Knocksheen outwitted a witch. The packman was a first-class entertainer with a propensity to flirt harmlessly with the ladies to the amusement and occasional annoyance of their menfolk, including the shepherd. Tales were told until Andrew said, 'Guid crack Sanny, but time for bed.'

'I'll juist feed the wean first,' said Helen, placing herself behind Sanny to avoid any embarrassment.

As there was only one bed, they all, as was the custom of the time, slept in it; the baby went back into the open bottom drawer. However, to accommodate common decency Helen got in first next to the wall, then Andrew, then Sanny. In no time at all the trio were fast asleep, lying like spoons in a drawer.

It had just passed midnight when the shepherd gave his wife a gentle dig in the ribs and whispered 'Ye'll need tae get up.'

'Whit's wrang?'

'It wis that beer; A need a pee.'

'Ye dinnae need me tae tak a pee.'

'Naw; bit yer nae steyin in the bed alane wi Sanny. It's no richt. If ye hae common decency, ye'll pit on yer goonie an cam wi me.'

With a sigh of exasperation Nel rose, lifted her dressing gown from behind the door and followed her husband outside. Both were blown down the kailyard to the wee hoose. Andrew went in and Nel sheltered in the lea, the corrugated sheet flapping and banging above her head. After a few minutes they returned to the house and slipped in past the snoring packman. Both were asleep in minutes.

An hour later the shepherd dug his wife in the ribs, 'Whit?' she complained.

'A need tae gang oot fer anither pee, sae ye'll need tae get up.'

'A'm no gettin up.'

'Ye cannae stey here, it's no decent.'

Nel stood her ground, 'A'm no gettin up, an that's final.'

The shepherd hissed through his teeth and climbed from the bed, tinges of jealousy playing in his mind. He tiptoed to the chest of drawers lifted out the baby and placed it between the packman and his wife. Pleased with his strategy, he went off for another pee. As he urinated, he was continually troubled by the banging above his head. Now it seemed a little worse. The thought that it might blow off and be lost irked him, 'Damn!' he said loudly, cursing himself for not sorting it earlier. 'Yae damn nail.'

Back at the house he lifted the baby and placed it back in the drawer then slipped quietly into bed, disturbing both his wife and the packman. He lay unable to sleep, the constant worry about the roof running in his mind, his ears alert to every bang. Now the wind was rising even more. Suddenly a roaring gust shook the thatch above and the sound of metal on metal as the sheet ripped away into the night. Without another thought, the shepherd leaped from his bed, threw on his coat and ran out into the storm, slamming the door behind, causing the stacked peat-fire to burst into flame. Both wife and packman sat upright and looked at each other. 'Nel looked at Sanny, smiled conspiratorially and said, 'Nou's yer chance.'

Sanny leaped from the bed, lifted the breadknife and cut himself a large slice of Dundee cake. 'Delicious!' he said cheerily.

2

A Bite in the Wind

The long-ago Celtic natives of *An Leargaidh Ghallda*, better known as Largs, were, like most Celts, fond of a good bonfire. Back in the Dark Ages – that's why they liked the bonfires – the king of Largs had his fiftieth birthday, so it was decided that they would go up the Gogo burn and build a great fire atop one of the hills at the head of the glen. What they didn't know was that many of Scotland's hills and mountains are, in fact, sleeping giants known as the Ettin. For the Ettin, a thousand-year sleep plus a two-hundred-year lie-in is not unusual, so when the Celts built their bonfire, little did they realise it was on the shoulder of an Ettin. Ceremoniously they gathered and hauled logs, branches and twigs to the top of the hill. With great pomp they marched in procession following a fiery torch. Once the fire was lit, they held hands and danced round the fire, singing:

> We are the Celts,
> Heederum Hoderum;
> We like to have a party,
> Heederum, Hoderum, Hoderum Hi.

Or something like that, but all in the local Celtic dialect. They were about to burst into a chorus and verse when the ground began to shake, then a mighty head rose up, turned and looked at them. 'Aagh! It's an ettin,' they cried and ran for their lives down into the glen. Now, like humans, the first thing an ettin likes to do is have some breakfast. When it saw the Celts running for home it climbed to its feet and lumbered after them saying in a great guttural voice in ettin-speak, 'A'm gaun tae eat ye. A'm gaun tae eat ye.'

'What are we going to do?' yelled the king, mainly because he had no idea what do.

Fortunately, they had a wise druid with them who said, 'Get a rope and we'll trip him up and then we'll chop his head off.' They grabbed lengths of ivy and quickly put together a long rope. Hiding among bushes they held it across the glen and managed to catch the foot of the Ettin. With a great 'Aagh!' he fell over and hit the ground with a mighty 'Thud!'. Quickly the Celts drew their swords and hacked his head off.

Now giants, especially the Ettin, are magic and so he managed, to the horror of the onlookers, to make his head pop back on. He picked himself to his feet and set off after them. 'A'm gaun tae eat ye. A'm gaun tae eat ye.'

'What are we going to do?' yelled the king, for he still had no idea what to do.

The wise druid said, 'Let's trip him up again and chop off his arms and legs and his head.'

'Do you think that will work?' said the king

'Why not? He fell for it before,' said the druid, managing not to laugh at his own pun.

They made the rope, hid in the bushes and stretched it out. Now Ettin's might be magical but unfortunately not logical; he tripped once again. Instantly he was surrounded by hacking Celts and his arms and legs and head were off. The pieces just sat there. But Ettins are a wee bit magical and quicker than they came off, they were on again. And he was off again, 'A'm gaun tae eat ye. A'm gaun tae eat ye.'

'What are we going to do?' said the king, who never knew what do at the best of times.

'He fell for the rope trick before,' said the druid, this time allowing himself a little grin, 'Let's do it again; this time we'll chop him into mince.'

The trip trap was duly set and the ettin was duly tripped. With swords, axes, knives and sharp stones the Celts set about chopping the ettin into tiny pieces. The giant was duly chopped until all that was left was an enormous, gory, pile of diced flesh. However (you know what's coming), yes, Ettins are magical, and to the wonderment and horror of all, the pieces knitted together in their hundreds and thousands. The sound was like someone rapidly slurping soup. You still know what's coming, and so did the Celts. In panic they rushed down to Largs as the brobdingnagian (good word that, eh?) brute lurched towards them, 'A'm gaun tae eat ye. A'm gaun tae eat ye.'

'What are we going to do?' said the king, who never had any idea what was going on, and why should he? He had advisors to do that, like the druid.

'This time we should trip him, chop him and burn him.'

'That's a bit harsh,' said the king.

'Well Sire, what could be worse than being attacked by an Ettin?'

The king thought for a while, 'Can't think of anything,' he said (that's what his advisors were for).

The Leargaidhach (that's the name for people who live in Largs) tripped him, chopped him, covered him in logs, branches and twigs and burned him. All that remained was a gargantuan (another big word for *big*, besides brobdingnagian) pile of ash. And it didn't move or join up or come together; it just sat there. It was a happy and relieved band of Celts that made their way home.

Out of curiosity one or two people visited the heap but it just sat there for a week. That was, until a wind from the East blew in and, on the way, it gathered up the ash and sent it skyward. In a great cloud it floated down the glen towards Largs. Now every fleck of ash was a little bit of giant and every speck was still hungering for breakfast and as they descended on the settlement each was filled with a voracious appetite and called out its teeny-weeny, tiny-winy voice, 'A'm gaun tae eat ye. A'm gaun tae eat ye.'

And that's how midges were invented.

Note: The king finally found out what the wise man didn't know: that there is something worse than being attacked by a giant. It's being attacked by a wee midget midge, especially in their millions – and they usually are.

3

A Chow in the Middle

Ayrshire Scots was often said to the purest form of Scots - largely by people from Ayrshire. Now, one young maid, employed in a country house, was so efficient at her job that her mistress decided to take the lass to her estate in England. 'There's only one thing bothers me, Betty,' said her ladyship, 'You speaking with such broad Ayrshire tongue; how do you expect to converse with English people?'

'Dinnae ye fash yersel, Milady, I'll juist miss oot the 'Rs' an chow the bits in the middle.'

4

A Spate o Milk

The miller of the Brig Mill at Girvan was a cheery fellow, the genuine jolly miller. His enthusiasm for life was such that he was always up before dawn to enjoy the best of the day. Out along the river the sun sparkled off the slow-moving current, swallows dipped and arced away, herons stalked frogs and minnows and the harsh call of crows made the silence between deeper; light dew soaked the toes of his boots as they swished through the cattle-grazed grass. A drystone dyke barred his way, so instead of leaping over he turned away from the river and up a gentle slope. He had gone some fifty yards when he heard the low murmur of a voice. It gave the impression of someone in prayer. He stopped, then walked on, this time lifting his feet to walk in silence. He reached the point where the voice came from and slowly keeked over the dyke. Below him, kneeling on the grass was Janet, the wife of the farmer of the land she knelt on. They, like everyone else, were subject to these hard times, though the woman and her husband seemed to have bountiful milk, cheese and butter. The miller presumed she was praying to God in thankfulness. As he watched and listened, he realised, in horror, that she was reciting an incantation:

> Mear's milk, an deer's milk, *mare*
> An every beast that bears milk
> Fra John o Groats tae Solway sea,
> Cam aa tae me; cam aa tae me.

Janet then scooped up dew from the grass and dropped it in her lap, then continued the incantation. In a moment of madness, the miller dropped to his knees and began whispering the incantation in time with Janet. The only difference was he recited:

Cam pairt tae me, cam pairt tae me. *part*

As he dropped the dew on his lap milk began to leak from his sleeve, then from his collar, it ran from under his bonnet. He stood up in horror as milk flowed out of his boots and from the bottom of his cutty breeks. In desperation he crept away homewards, leaving a trail of milk in his wake. He burst into his house and stood in the middle of the room, a large puddle growing at his feet. His wife, who was up making porridge, looked on in horror. Not a woman to waste anything, she called their children, a boy and two girls, who were ordered to find any container they could. In no time there were milk boins, bowies, bickers, cans, churns and cogs all full of warm creamy milk, and still it flowed. The children ran to neighbours, who arrived with more containers, and they too were filled to overflowing. The miller was still in a state of shock and none too pleased that everyone was having a laugh at his expense, 'Ye're the best coo in the byre,' said his wife before folding over in laughter. This did little to ease the miller's despair and he sank to his knees, not knowing what species or sex he was: 'A'm a coo,' he wailed.

'Naw,' declared his wife, 'Mair a herd o coos, Jock,' almost keeling over in hysterics along with everyone else.

Now there was such a proverbial deluge of milk that items of furniture began to float towards the door and the house was in serious threat of inundation. Jock's wife ordered everyone to carry her husband outside. Soon the milk was tumbling into their mill lade and down into the Girvan Water.

Meanwhile, Janet, who had finished her incantations, was making her way home. As she reached the river, she saw the whiteness spreading down the stream and stared at it in curiosity. She then made her way upstream pondering its possibilities. She reached the mill and saw the stream of milk falling into the river. Now she suspected that her incantations played some part in it. Following this, and the sound of Jock's wailing, she came upon a scene of chaos. For now, the hilarity had ceased, and people were worried as to Jock's future. He was now sitting upright on a small knoll so that the milk flowed past his house and mill. As she appeared, Jock raised an accusing finger, 'Ye are witch and are deservit o bein brunt.' The last word was spat out.

Seeing all the hostile faces, and filled with the urge to run, she decided to stand her ground. Janet raised a finger at Jock, 'Then that'll mak twae o us. Ye are as guilty as me o cantrips.'

Jock protested, 'But…' then realised the truth of the statement. He was also desperate to be rid of the glamourie. He gave Janet a pleading look. 'Gin ye stop this curse, a'll say naethin.' He looked about, 'An that gangs fer the rest o ye; nor ye get yer grain millt.' The small crowd nodded their assent.

Janet turned her back and quietly muttered the counter-spell that released Jock. As people dispersed and normality returned, the miller took the witch aside, 'Nae mair o yer cantrips Janet, an a promise a'll neer reveal it tae onybody. These are hard times an aabody needs tae be rewarded fer their darg, an no hae it thieved wi cantrips.'

'Aye, fair do. An a'll no reveal them either, lest some bairn or fool is temptit tae meddle wi dangerous things.'

'Richt eneugh,' said Jock; then the underlying meaning of her words sunk in. 'Aye, that'l mak twae o us.' They both laughed hard at the truth of it.

5
Ailsa Craig

Ailsa Craig, they say, is a volcanic plug and stands ten miles off the Carrick coast. It belongs to the parish of Dailly and is most famous for being a bird sanctuary and for providing the best curling stones from its blue-hone granite. The writer's grandfather, Alick McQuater, used to travel to the island and choose his own stones. Craig is Gaelic, usually meaning a rocky mountain. The Ailsa part is probably Norse. Strictly speaking it is Ailsey, the ey part meaning island. Some have suggested that is from the Gaelic aillse meaning fairy. This is unlikely as the common word for fairy in Scottish Gaelic is sith, pronounced shee - Glenshee, Schiehallion, Knocksheen, etc.
Back to the volcanic plug: my mother told me this is scientific nonsense and she was always right - she told me that too. The truth is that the Irish giant Fionn MacCumhall was quarrelling with the Scottish giant CuChullaine. The result was a battle of the boulders, one of which missed and landed in the sea, ten miles off Carrick.

Sometimes known as Paddy's Milestone, it was also used by the Gruagach of Arran as a stepping stone. She lived at East Bennan on the south of Arran and, like the brownie, happily cared for the local people's cattle. Eventually, someone, ignorant in the way of brownies and gruagachs, decided to reward her. She took it as an insult and departed by placing her left foot on Beinn Buidhe on Arran and the other on Ailsay with the intention of stepping over to Carrick. Alas, a high-masted ship passed beneath her, striking her in the nether region and she fell into the sea and drowned. Sad.

6
Alexander the Dagger

In folklore one of the great characters is the trickster. Whether it be the jackal of Asia, the Crow in Australia, Kulalu the Hare and Anansi spider in Africa, coyote in America or Loki in the Norse myths of Europe, there is no story without him or her. The following tale is essentially a trickster tale, likely to be apocryphal, though something of it rings true.

In the late Medieval period young men from wealthy families, when not practising for war, were prone to commit pranks on all and sundry. While not endearing themselves to their victims, these knights errant thought such practices great fun and endlessly carried them out. Young Alexander Kennedy of Dunure or, as he was known, Alschunder Dalgour, was one such young man with too much time on his hands. His nickname Dalgour, or dagger, was given because of his skill with a short sword. However, his continual practical joking led to a falling out with the Earl of Wigtown. Frustrated by his continual irritations, the Earl put out a proclamation that whoever brought him the head of the young knight would be rewarded with forty-merk lands at Stewarton in Ayrshire. Dalgour, hearing of the reward, made himself scarce, but knew that sooner or later someone would act on it and so constructed a plan. He gathered a band of youngbloods and made his way to Wigtown, arriving on a Sunday. The earl, as was his religious duty, attended early mass. The band of young men placed themselves on either side of the entrance and waited. After mass, as the earl left the building with some companions, the knights surrounded him. Dalgour gave a low, exaggerated bow, 'A fine sabbath mornin, Your Lordship. Alas we were a wee bittie late for mass.'

The unarmed earl knew he was in mortal danger but held his ground and gave Dalgour a steely look, 'And whit brings ye doon these pairts, young Kennedy?'

'A hear that there is a reward offerit fer ma heid.' His attitude was overly cocky.

'Aye!'

'Weel here it is,' said the young man pointing upwards with both index fingers, 'It is, as ye can see, attachit tae ma body. But ma heid it maist certainly is, an a claim the reward.'

There was a gasp of incredulity from the earl's companions. Wigtown, on the other hand, pulled momentarily at his beard then a grin broke across his face. He shook his head, 'O aa the bare-faceit affronteries, A hae ne'er seen the like. Ye hae bestit me, an a am amuisit.' The smile slipped from his face and the steeliness returned. 'Nou tak yer heid, an the land. But tak heed: gin ye cross me anither time the ootcam will be assurit.'

Dalgour dropped the cocky demeanour, 'A am pleasit that a hae humourit ye, Yer Lordship; an gratefu fer yer indulgence.' He gave a humble bow and with a nod to his companions turned and hastened away to their horses.

At a distance the companions broke into laughter and slapped Dalgour across the back. As they rode north, he laughed with them for a little, then slipped into a more serious mood. He had a foreboding that his end would not be far away.

Alschunder Dalgour slipped back into his old ways; in the end he irritated not only his enemies but his friends. They came for him one night and smothered him beneath his pillow.

7

Any Bottle of Port in a Storm

In 1820, a reverend gentleman in the fair land of Carrick was invited to a function in Maybole by local farmers. Now farmers are not unknown to enjoy a tipple and some a few; but even the hardest of these hard drinkers was astonished at the amount of wine the good minister consumed. A short time later, one of the farmers was talking to a colleague and remarked on the minister's alcoholic consumption. 'Sax bottles o port he pit awa, John. Sax!'

'Yer haiverin Alick. The guid reverent doctor is fond o a wee bittie wine, but noo yer slanderin him.'

'A'm daein nae sic a thing. A wis there an a saw it wae ma ain een.'

It wuid be yer ain consumpt man, ye wur seein dooble.'

'Sax John.'

'It's no possible.'

'It's possible an it's true, an a'm prepared tae wager on it.'

'A'll tak the wager at the price o sax bottles o port.'

'Duin!'

Without any more ado the friends strode towards the manse which lay some miles away. John knocked on the door and the minister's housekeeper, answered, 'Is Mr Duguid at hame, Mavis?'

'Aye he is. He's busy in the study but a'll juist go an see if he is appen tae see ye.'

A moment later Mavis returned, 'If ye'll juist come in, he'll see ye noo. It's the seicont door on the left.'

Both gentlemen entered and, a little nervously, walked to the study door. Alick knocked. 'Enter,' came an authoritarian voice. Both men entered. The minister bade them have a seat while he stood, his back to the fire. 'Whit can a dae fer ye gentlemen?'

The men looked at each other before John, after a few 'Em, ems,' said, We hae cam tae ask ye a gey queer question.'

'An that is?'

'Weel meenister, ye see, it's tae settle a wager.' The minister raised a disapproving eyebrow. 'Juist a freenly yin atween freens, ye ken,' said John, his face turning red with embarrassment. 'A hope ye'll no tak it amiss.'

'We'll see,' said the reverend, a mischievous twinkle in his eye.

Alick took up the reins, 'It is this sir: hoo mony bottles o port did ye drink the ither day at the fermer's do? Ye see, a bet John Williamson here thet it wis six bottle o port. John wagered that ye didnae.'

'Weel, alas Alick, ye hae lost the bet. A only drank five bottles o port.' Reverend Duguid paused a moment, 'The saxth was a bottle o sherry.'

8
The Auld Brig

Marian and Mary Crauford had ordered the servants to lock and bar all the doors of their castle- keep near the mouth of the River Ayr, for the Firth of Clyde was dotted with the sails of birlinns and longships of King Haco of Norway. The Norwegian monarch was on a quest to show the upstart King of Scots, Alexander III, who was the real power on the west coast of Scotland. The major part of the fleet was moored between Holy Island and Arran waiting for the king's instructions, while marauders harried and intimidated the coastline. The sisters knew that they could withstand a short-term assault but prayed that the Norsemen would go elsewhere to wreak vengeance. An army of Scots had gathered at An Leargaidh Ghallda, hoping to draw the Viking to a place where they had the advantage of height. Among the knights with the king were Richard de Boyle of Kelburn and Alexander Fraser who were betrothed to the sisters.

That night both sisters prayed for the safekeeping of their lovers and in the morning sent a young squire, Allan Boyd, off to Largs to report on the progress of the coming battle. When Allan reached Fairlie he could see that the fighting was intense. Unarmed, except for a shortsword, he wisely stayed where he was and observed the action for a time, but could not see which side had the advantage. Even when the Norsemen took to their ships and began to sail away, he wasn't convinced of a Scots victory. He made his way to the battleground searching for de Boyle and Fraser among the heaps of dead bodies. Happily, he found the young knights still alive, though spent from exhaustion. The squire passed on the compliments of Marian and Mary and thanked God that the knights had been spared death.

The king rallied the remains of his army and gave an unconvincing victory speech. He praised the bravery of all those who had taken part and mourned the loss of those who had given the ultimate sacrifice. Young Allan then set off

at great haste to inform the waiting sisters of the fate of their fiancées. When he reached the River Ayr, he plunged into the shallows just above the castle, waving his bonnet and yelling to anyone who would listen that Scotland had won the day and the victors would soon be home safely. When he reached the keep, he ran up the stairs, two at a time, stopping only briefly at the door before rushing in and proclaiming the joyous news. The sisters danced with happiness and ordered that bunting be hung from the castle walls and every available flag flown to welcome home the gallant knights. That night in the hills of eastern Kyle a thunderous rain fell, streams became torrents and the rushing waters swelled the river to bursting. The spate ran to the sea and in time, with an incoming tide, the estuary level rose high, coinciding with the arrival young Richard de Boyle, Alexander Fraser and their company. Out of keenness to be home with their lovers and part bravado, the troop threw itself into the surging stream. Fraser's horse missed its footing on rock and stumbled. The force of the water threw the knight into the water, at the same time his horse rammed into de Boyle's charger causing it to fall; the weight of chainmail and weapons pulled both men under. Their colleagues attempted a rescue, only to be dragged down themselves. All this was enacted in front of the horrified and helpless sisters.

Days later, the sea gave up the bodies of the unfortunate knights. They and their companions were buried in the church grounds with due pomp and ceremony. The sisters in their grief swore an oath of chastity and resolved never to marry. As a memorial to their doomed lovers they had a bridge built which was, in its time, the New Bridge. History has assigned it another title, The Auld Brig o Ayr.

The date of the earliest building of the bridge, which was in the early thirteenth century, does not accord with the date of the Battle of Largs 1263. However, the legend persists and may well be based on events following another earlier battle.

9
Ayrshire Bluebeard Faus Sir John

Sir John Cathcart of Carleton Castle at Lendalfoot in Carrick was a ruthless, yet immensely charming man. In the time of our tale the laird had lost seven wives. One might assign a certain carelessness to him, but in truth their loss was at his own hands. His motive was, quite simply, greed. The idea had come to him early-on when he had pretended to push his new wife off the two-hundred feet cliff of Game's Loup and ended doing just that. He was, of course, horrified but managed to charm his way out of it, saying she had gone too close to the edge and slipped. Still a young man and now widowed, tradition demanded he get an heir, so he looked about for another suitable candidate. With his first wife had come a substantial dowry, so he sought out similar. The eldest unmarried daughter of a laird at Kirkmichael suited the bill, so he wooed and won her. After a year she was neither with child and his occasional gambling had depleted the dowry to such a degree his thoughts turned to murder.

'It's sic a pleisant day, ma dear, a thocht we micht tak a picnic and enjoy oor pleisant scenery.'

That wuid be a delite,' she said, little knowing her fate.

He took the unsuspecting woman on a picnic to Game's Loup, the scene of the earlier tragedy. The walk to the clifftop view took half an hour as they strolled, chatted and laughed.

'It's sae bonny John: Ailsey and Arran. What's that ayont? she asked.

'That's Cantyre; an on a guid day ower there,' he said, pointing south west, 'ye can see Erin.'

She stared in the direction of his finger, 'Aa a can see is a loom.'

With his heart pounding and a strange thrill of excitement, he put his right arm about her shoulder, 'Luik there, ye can juist see the hills o Antrim.'

As she raised a hand to her eyes to shield the sky Cathcart propelled her over the cliff. He heard her sudden intake of breath followed by a prolonged scream that ended abruptly as she bounced off a rock into the sea and lay shattered among the waves.

'Sic a waste,' he muttered, 'I cuid hae gotten a few shillins fer the dress.'

He thought of the strange question his old warrior grandfather had asked him as a boy, 'Whit is worse, tae kill yin or tae kill mony?'

'To kill mony,' he had responded.

'Nae laddie. It is worse to kill yin.'

He had puzzled the question and the old man's answer many times. Now he knew him to be right. It is the first that is the worst. After that, it gets easier. And easier it was for Cathcart. He took another wife, then another, sending them to their doom. All that is except one who, on fleeing his growing madness, fell to her death on the Byne Hill above Girvan. A place now known as the Maiden's Bed.

These were savage times, but his activities were beyond the pale, having directly or indirectly dispensed with seven wives, each time gathering substantial dowries. That he was not put under any suspicion was due to the high death rate among people, especially women at childbirth. On one occasion, to disguise his nefarious deed, he went to the home of his late spouse and threatened her family that they should return his wife to him. That she lay, food for the fishes, among the waves of Game's Loup made this highly unlikely. However, rumours of his deeds circulated, and people began to avoid him and his evil residence. But this did not stop the Dark Laird seeking out another victim. He discovered that his cousin, the Laird of Collain was looking for a husband for his youngest daughter, May. She was not a bonny lass, and worse, she had an independent spirit and was bright and sharp-witted. This little concerned Cathcart as he was more interested in the dowry. Being independent and sharp-witted did not include the ability to fly.

To disguise her plainness her mother and father dressed her in the finest silk dresses and delicate shoes from France. Her neck, wrists, ankles and finger were bedecked with gold and silver of the most exquisite filigree and her bonnets and coats, though of wool, were of the finest quality and covered in elaborate silk embroidery. On her wedding day she looked almost beautiful and her dowry, delivered in a coach, looked to Sir John even more beautiful. As she was the daughter of his cousin, he thought it wise to have her live a decent time before dispatching her. However, May proved to be more than a handful. Her independence was an affront to the laird who thought that woman should be decorative and run the household. She did, but on her terms. Before long Sir John seemed less the master of the house and more the second-in-command. Known for his quick temper it was galling for him to be matched, and often bested, by the quick-witted May, whose tongue was often sharper than Spanish steel. After nine months he had enough and wanted her away.

As before, he suggested they walk out to take the air. 'Dae ye no hae suitable claes fer the promenade? It micht get a bit clarty? Aiblins some auld garments?'

May looked at him coldly, 'A wis raisit a lady o means John. A wull juist hae tae gang as a am, an you maun replace them frae the siller gien wi me, suid they suffer.'

The thought of spending more money on her raised his hackles, but he stilled his temper, 'There micht be nae need fer extravagance, ma dearie.' He turned away, a leer of hate and intent crossed his face.

The walk was done mainly in silence. Every few yards May would stop and pick wildflowers which she laid in her basket. 'Sic braw things, they will mak a bonny garland fer my bed.'

'Can ye no pick them on the wey back? The sun will be doun afore we get there.'

'Hou faur are we gaun, Glenapp?'

He shook his head,' Naw, Game's Loup.'

'Whit a strynge name. Whit daes it mean?'

'I hae nae idea, though ma granfaither said it wis whaur the savages o lang ago wuid drive deer aff the cliff insteid o tryin to kill them wi bow an spear. But that micht juist be a fairy tale.'

'Is it a muckle drap, like Collain?' asked May.

'Naw. But juist as final.'

There was something in the way he said it that sent a chill through May, but still she followed him.

They reached the Loup and without hesitation he turned to her, 'Tak yer claes aff!'

'But John, this is hardly the place and time, an a wee bittie tenderness wuid gang a lang wey.'

'It is no tenderness ye will get, it is the end o ye. I hae cuist aa ma wives but yin ower this precipice and nou ye will jyne them, so strip! And be shuir tae tak aff yer jewellery as weel.'

'John, oh John, een in this direst o mauments ye are still a gentleman; sae, dae the honourable thing and turn yer back as a undress.

The laird gave a sigh and turned to face the sea. In that moment May boldly stepped forward and gave the man a mighty push over the edge. She heard the intake of breath then a howl rent the air as False Sir John Cathcart plummeted onto the rocky shore of Carrick.

This is obviously a Bluebeard-type tale which is of French origin and thought to be based on real people. In folklore it is classed as Type 312 in the Aarne-Thompson classification system. Two very similar versions of this tale exist for the town of Ayr. They were kept alive in Gaelic on South Uist and are probably passed-on tales by mariners based on the ballad, Faus Sir John:

In Ayr castle there lived a king who had married out of duty and political reasons and not for love - a common tradition in the past. When going about his kingly duties he met a beautiful lady of nobility and fell in love. Out of expedience he made his wife disappear and married the woman. However, history repeated itself after meeting a more beautiful woman than his second wife. During his third marriage he grew tired of his wife and sought to dispose of her. In the castle was an Irishman whom the king used as an advisor due to his vast experiences in the internal wars of Ireland. One day the Irishman stopped by a door after hearing a voice inside. He listened and realised it was the king talking to himself, 'Hou shoud A rid maself o this woman? Hou? Hou? Hou?' The Irishman, who had grown extremely fond of the queen slipped away and went to her chamber to warn her.

'Thank ye, Col; A will be on ma gaird at aa times an shoud a need yer services again, please be prepared.'

'Yes, Your Majesty,'

When the king was out riding one day he passed by a seemingly bottomless sinkhole and a plan fell into place. The next day he encouraged his wife to join him in cross-country ride. On the way back, they just happened to pass the sinkhole. 'What a strynge thing,' he said, climbing from the horse. He peered into the hole than turned to his wife, 'Cam an hae a luik.' He helped the queen dismount and escorted her to the hole. She made sure she was a distance from him as she peered into the darkness. 'Whit is that?' she said, pointing into the mirk. Out of curiosity, the king walked to where she was and peered down. Now was her chance and she pushed him clean over the edge. His yell echoed in the depths before the sound of a body hitting solid ground, then silence.

In case she was implicated in the king's death, the queen arranged to sail off to Ireland with her saviour. In time the castle was sold for a great sum, but no one ever lived in it again.

10

CARRICK, KYLE, CUNNINGHAM, AND GALLOWAY.

Carrick for a man,
Kyle for a coo,
Cunningham for corn and bere, *barley*
An Galloway for woo. *wool*

The rhyme speaks for itself and indicates the strengths of each of the districts

DUNDONALD

Donald Din
Built his hoose without a pin.

There stauns a caustle i the west,
They caa it Donald Din;
There's no a nail in aa its roof,
Nor yet a wuiden pin.

SUNDRUM

Sundrum sall sink, *shall*
Auchincruive sall faa, *fall*
And the name o Cathcart
Sall in time wear awa !

THE WEE YOWE

There wis a wee yowe, *ewe*
Hippin frae knowe to knowe: *hopping*
It lookit up tae the mune,

And saw mae ferlies na fyfteen: *wonders*
It tuik a fit in ilka hand,
An hippit awa' to Airland; *hopped*
Frae Airland to Aberdeen:
An whan the yowe cam hame again,
The gudeman was outbye herdin the kye; *farmer, cows*
The swine were in the spence, makin the whey; *scullery*
The gudewife was butt an' ben, tinklin the keys, *in the house, piano*
And lookin ower lasses makin at the cheese;
The cat in the asse-hole, makin at the brose— *ashpit*
Down fell a cinner, and burnt the cat's nose,
And it cried Yeowe, yeowe, yeowe, &c.

THE WEE WIFIE

TUNE—*The Rock and the Wee Pickle Tow*

There was a wee wifie, row't up in a blanket,
Nineteen times as hie as the moon ;
And what did she there I canna declare,
For in her oxter she bure the sun. *carried*

'Wee wifie, wee wifie, wee wifie,' quo I,
'Oh, what are ye doin' up there sae hie?'
'I'm blawin the cauld cluds out o' the lift:' *cold clouds*
'Weel dune, weel dune, wee wifie!' quo' I.

This was also a popular children's song across Britain
'There was an Old Woman went up in a basket'

KATIE BEARDIE

Katie Beardie had a coo,
Black and white about the mou;
Wasna that a dentie coo? *daintie*
Dance, Katie Beardie!

Katie Beardie had a hen,
Cackled butt and cackled ben ; *barn and house*
Wasnae that a dentie hen?
Dance, Katie Beardie!

Katie Beardie had a cock,
That could spin backin rock; *brushed wool*
Wasna that a dentie cock?
Dance, Katie Beardie !

Katie Beardie had a grice, *pig*
It could skate upon the ice;
Wasna that a dentie grice?
Dance, Katie Beardie !

AYR BAY FISH

When the muin is roon an fair, *moon*
The fishes swim fae Troon tae Ayr.
When the muin is fair and roon,
The fishes swim fae Ayr tae Troon.

THE HEIDMAISTER

Oor schuil's a bonny wee schuil, *school*
It's made o bricks an plaister;
The only thing that's wrang wi it
Is the bauldy-heidit maister.
He gangs tae the pub oan Seturday nicht,
He gangs tae the kirk oan Sunday,
He prays tae the Lord tae gie him strength
Tae batter us oan Muinday.

THE COO

Upon a hill thir stauns a coo *stands*
It maun hae moved, it's no there nou. *must*

MAYBOLE

Meybole's a stinkin hole,
Kirmickel's fou o ashes; *full*
Crosshill's a bonnie wee place,
Wi bonnie lads an lassies.

When Girvan was a sandy knowe *hillock*
And Crosshill lay beneath the plough,
And Dailly stood - no one knows how-

Stood the auld toon o Maybole.

Minniebole's a dirty hole,
It sits abune a mire, *above*
But to me and hundreds like me
It's the finest in the shire.

Minniebole's a dirty hole,
Ayr is fou o clashes, *waterlogged holes*
Girvan is a bonnie toon
Wi bonnie lads and lassies.

Minniebole's a gran wee place,
It sits langside a hill,
Tis there ye get the finest claith
An' mutchkins o guid yill. *¾ of a pint, ale*

If ye should gae tae Maybole toon,
Your jaunt will no be wasted,
Gin ye should buy a pair o shoon *shoes*
They're the finest ever lasted.

CARRICK

Twixt Wigton and the toon o Ayr *between*
Portpatrick and the cruives o Cree, *fishing stakes*
You shall not get a lodging there,
Except ye court a Kennedy.

OCCASIONAL RHYMES AND PLACES

'Johnnie Smith o Minniebole
Can ye shoe a wee foal?'
'Yes, indeed, an that a can,
Just as weel as ony man.'

Pit a wee bit on the tae
Fur tae mak' him sklim the brae; *climb*
Pit a wee bit on the heel
Fur tae mak him trot weel,

Trot weel, trot weel, trot weel
Hame again!

In Maybole toon thae leeved a man,
They ca'd him Bailie Niven,
Wha gathered muckle gear and Ian
But never got tae Heaven.

William Niven was a real person and a friend of Robert Burns

Yae mornin a got early up,
Ah cambed and brushed ma hair, sir, *combed*
And aff a set wi aa ma micht *might*
Intae Girvan toon, sir.

Frae Dinnimuck and Weary Neuk
An aa alang the shore, man,
And sic a day in Girvan toon
Ye never kent afore, man. *knew before*

Gettin up Auld Dailly Brae
We had an awfy wark, man, *awful work*
An when we reachit auld Penkill
We wur strippit tae the sark, man. *shirt*

11

Gypsies, or Roma, were part of the Indo-European peoples that, in the 3rd Century BC, migrated both east and west from the Caucasus and can be found all the way from India to Ireland. The Roma themselves were likely a dispossessed ethnic group from northern India. The term Gypsy, because they were assumed to come from Egypt, though still used as a legal term, is now largely considered unacceptable or even racist and the name Roma or Romany is the preferred usage.
In these times also, estates and rights to the land passed to the first-born son by what is known as primogeniture.

Meg Cunninghame muttered to herself in Scottish cant as she walked the banks of the Girvan, while all about her a chorus of birdsong filled the soft spring air. She was reciting the names of the plants that passed underfoot. She knew them all and their properties, from bitter to aromatic and poisonous to health-giving. She was also bestowed with a heart of kindness and gentleness that belied a core of steel. She had survived the hardships of a travelling life and was destined to outlive all her peers; but for now, she was intent in finding a suitably scented posy that she might sell for a few bawbees to the good lady of Bargany. The old Romany knew she was a kind, but put-upon, woman who would also, if her husband were not about, send her down to the kitchen for soup and a fardel of oatcake. Lord Bargany, on the other hand, was a narcissistic, self-serving, shilpit, mean creature inclined to making those around him miserable. He continuously threatened to raise rents and corn-grinding fees at his mill. As fate would have it the rider whom she saw approaching in the distance turned out to be that very man. Out of good manners, and with a dash of self-preservation, she curtsied him, 'Guid day, sir. A fine day to be oot ridin.'

'It was until now,' he said, sarcastically, 'Why are you walking on my land?'

'A am on an errand tae the guid lady o Bargany wi a scentit posy.'

'Begging, that's what you are doing. We'll have no beggars and more especially Egyptians.' He raised his whip and made to strike her. With a nimbleness that belied her age, she sidestepped the strike and ran out past the lord towards a thicket of hawthorn. He turned the horse about and raced after her catching up as she reached the bushes.

As she entered the thicket, her skirts caught on the thorns and held her a moment. It was enough for Bargany to leap from his horse and lay into her with the whip. Above them a carrion crow's harsh call echoed through the trees. Limp with the pain of the thrashing she fell among the thorns that ripped her hands and face. Bloodied but unbowed, she drew on her inner strength and faced him with defiance, 'A curse on ye Lord Bargany that frae this day the corbies will lea Bargany neer tae return, an ye sall hae nocht but dochters an wives. Nae laddie, nae heir sall be born within the waas o Bargany intil kindness returns. Then, and only then, will the corbies return.'

Bargany gave a laugh of derision and climbed back on to his horse and, filled with his own Presbyterian certainty, instantly forgot about the crime he had just perpetrated. With his self-absorbed view on the world, he never noticed that neither raven, crow, rook, jackdaw, magpie or jay came within the precincts of the estate and though the lord tried, no male heir was delivered. To his misogynistic displeasure, only girls were born within the walls of Bargany and eventually, when he died, the estate went to a cousin; still the *corvidae* did not return. Generations later the estate and title passed to yet another relative; but this young man was of a different order. He carried with him a sense of humanity and an understanding that without the good will of the people about him, things would inevitably fail. He and his equally good-natured wife set about improving the land and the living conditions of the people that worked for him. The notoriety of Carrick's poverty was soon a thing of the past and others followed suit. He was also not averse to rolling up his sleeves and taking to the pick and shovel. He led by example and was shown great love and respect.

One spring morning he and his wife set out for a ride along the banks of the Girvan. The water ran clear and they could see the salmon lined up in the pools waiting for the next deluge that would take then all the way to Tairlaw. The air was soft with a gentle coolness and the birds sang merrily in the trees and bushes. With raised spirits they rode and chatted. Ahead an elderly bent figure walked slowly towards them. As they reached her, the Lord and Lady stopped and greeted her, 'Good morning,' they each said.

'It' s a sweet morning to be out,' he added

'Aye it is sir.'

'Do you have such a thing as a diamond or a ruby necklace to grace the neck of my dear wife.' He said, a teasing twinkle in his eye.

'Aiblins a dae yer lordship. If ye wull permit me a meenit yer grace, A wull hae a luik among ma geegaws.'

The old woman untied the blanket on her back and laid out her wares, 'Nou, let me see! Ah! The very thing.' She picked up a necklace of exquisitely twisted grasses from which hung turretella and periwinkle shells and handed it up to the new Lord Bargany.

He tied it about his wife's elegant neck, 'Perfect!' said the young man. He put his hand into his waistcoat and drew out a coin, leaned down hand slipped it into the old woman's hand, 'Alas I cannot cross you palm with silver, but perhaps this might serve you as well.'

Meg Cunninhame opened her hand and in the palm sat a small gold half-guinea. A fortune to such as she.

'Ye are a guid folk Lord an Lady Bargany an deservin o guid fortun.' She stepped off the track and with a knife she kept in her waistband she cut a branch of broom. With this she swept the path in front of the riders. 'There! A hae brushit awa the ill luck that has cursit yer hoose these lang years. Suin ye sall hae an heir.'

'Thank you, good woman. Walk on to the house and go to the kitchen and see Betty the cook and she will set you right for a good meal.'

'Thank ye kindly, yer grace and yer ladyship. May guid fortun bless yer days.'

It was later that day when Lord and Lady Bargany arrived back at their home. As they approached the house Bargany turned to his wife. You know, that's the first time I've seen jackdaws on the chimneys. '

'Yes,' she said, 'and rooks in the trees.'

As they dismounted a crow flew close by and two ravens passed calling in their distinctive 'kronk'. An heir, their first child, was born the following spring.

12

The Black Dog of Glenapp

It is said that on certain nights when the moon rides hard against the wind and clouds run for their lives, a great slavering black dog haunts the road through Glenapp. Drivers tell of its sudden appearance and disappearance. Some say it is a trick of moonlight, some say it is for real. Perhaps when the moon is up and rides hard against the wind, and clouds run for their lives, it is time to take the road through Glenapp and see for yourselves.

13

The Brandy Hole

In eighteenth century Scotland - and before - the taxation of whisky was seen as a greedy imposition by the government on a God-given right to distil your own liquor. Because of this, and excessively high taxes, smuggling became a national pastime. Preferring the name 'free- traders', an industry grew; with timber, and even tea, from Scandinavia, salt from Northern Ireland and spirits and wine from the Netherlands. The Isle of Man, which was independent at the time, was a key base for smuggling tobacco and brandy into Galloway and Ayrshire and fast excise cutters patrolled the Solway and the Firth of Clyde on the lookout for contraband. Every bay and sandy beach, especially those with a convenient cave, saw its fair share of nightly action; but gradually these were discovered, and more and more ingenious methods were used to hide the illicit goods. Apart from lofts and cellars, which were easily discovered, false walls, hidden passages, traps under fire-places or beneath bad-tempered livestock were created. Any hole in the ground on a farm or croft was adapted to store such goods. These were usually referred to as smuggle-holes or brandy-holes.

William MacAdam, an elder of the kirk in Dundonald, accidentally discovered the whereabouts of such a stash on a local farm, and on a dark Sunday night he helped himself to a barrel of brandy and a kist of tobacco which he temporarily hid in a disused barn. As he sat in his kitchen thinking about the ill-gotten goods he was stricken by guilt and remorse. Firstly, he had broken the Sabbath, but he was also guilty of theft, even if it was contraband. He was not much of a drinker and could not involve others by sharing it, and there was enough tobacco to last him two lifetimes. What was he to do? He was sure that the brandy hole would now be watched, so he could not put it back, yet he felt obliged to return it. How? The idea came slowly and pleased his sense of humour.

On Friday night he wandered into the hostelry that the smuggling farmer frequented and sat down at the same table, 'A wee burd telt me ye lost some gear Jackie,' he said.

'Aye Willie, some ratton helpit himsel. We'll fin oot wha it wis an rin him oot the district.'

'Aye,' said the elder, 'serves him richt, whaever he is.' Our errant hero paused a moment then said, 'A'm gaun intae Kilmarnock on Seturday an a ken a woman they say has the seicont sicht: a spaewife. A cuid ask her.'

'That's a guid idea Wull,' said the farmer.

'It'll cost a guinea,' replied William

'A guinea ye say. A lot o money, but a barrel o brandy an a kist o baccy's a damn sicht mair.' The reluctant farmer handed over the cash.

McAdam went off to Kilmarnock as promised; not to see any spaewife, but rather to visit a local hostelry where he enjoyed a few legal glasses of brandy and the company of a woman who was not his wife. On his return to Dundonald he met up with the farmer and some friends and related his tryst with the unholy. He told of strange apparitions, the smell of brimstone and hellish noises coming from all about. Eventually, he said that the spaewife, all in a dwam, had revealed that the lost merchandise could be found in an auld barn, half a mile along the Dreghorn track; but not before he had paid her another guinea. The farmer duly paid up and the party set out. The barn was located and the group found the untouched goods.

There were others about who also lost goods from their brandy holes and MacAdam elected to visit the spaewife on their behalf, for the price of a guinea, and perhaps another: they, being too fearful of the Devil and his hordes of demons. They knew that an upright member of the kirk could face the denizens of Hell and come away unscathed. And so, Willie MacAdam prospered in his deceit.

How he managed to square such a string of immoral conceits against his position as an elder of the kirk is anybody's guess. Then again, he wasn't the only Holy Willie.

14

Bride's Bed

A young woman set out from Loch Doon on her way to the Water of Minnoch to meet with her sweetheart and be married. On the way she was caught in a snowstorm and took shelter in a hollow. Alas the hollow filled with snow and she died from exposure. The place is now called the Bride's Bed

15

It was one of those cold, drizzly days when the air hangs with water and trees drip incessantly. The peat fire in the ingle was weak and only small murmurs of heat rose from the faint embers. We were all gathered about it, miserable and cold, when a voice at the window said, 'Rise, let me in; I'm hungry an weary an wat tae the skin.' Mum opened the door, while we tried to fan some life into the fire for our unknown guest. When he walked in our jaws dropped, literally. Before us stood a wee hairy man, and when I say hairy, I mean thick hair from his head to his feet. He was dressed, if that's the right word, in skins from the polecat and the fox which tried to out-compete each other for the worst smell. Dad, never the bravest of men, ran for the door. Thanks Dad. What about us? Anyway, the thing seemed harmless, at least to me, and spoke in a rasp, but with a gentle air, 'Gie me wark an aa the wages a will eer seek is a cog fu o brose.' My brothers and sisters weren't so sure of him and retreated into the recessed bed. Mother, more in fear, nodded her agreement and the wee creature disappeared back through the door, at which point Dad shot back in.

The following morning there was no sight of him, but the stable had been mucked out, the corn thrashed, the cows brought in from the hill, water carried in from the stream and the fire made ready. For a year the work was done over-night and our lives became a little easier. He took the corn to the mill and penned the sheep: he even managed to herd in half a dozen hares and two moorhens. As was his due, Mum always made sure there was a cog of brose on the doorstep last thing at night. Though we saw neither hide nor hair of him, by the morning the brose was gone, and the work done. Gradually our wee croft began to prosper and for the first time we had shoon for our feet and a coat for the winter.

Though Mum insisted we tell no one of our good fortune, word soon got out and spread through the district. It was only a matter of time before we had a visit from the minister who berated Mum and Dad for engaging in ungodly practices. They took the telling-off but were in no mind to lose our wee friend. However, after the minister's visit, the broonie, for that's what he was, never returned and the brose remained untouched and the work undone. It was a few weeks before Dad noticed something above the door lintel and, pulling it out, discovered a wee Bible. Around the open book we all sat and prayed for our wee helper, silently cursing the self-righteous minister, then returned to poverty.

16

Burns and Folktale

Robert Burns was a lover of folklore and folktales and mentions so in a biographical letter to Dr John Moore where he says, 'I owed much to [Betty Davidson], an old Maid of my mother's [who] had, I suppose, the largest collection in the country of tales and songs concerning devils, ghosts, fairies, brownies, witches, warlock, spunkies, kelpies, elf-candles, dead-lights, wraiths, apparitions, cantraips, giants, enchanted towers, dragons and other such trumpery. This cultivated the latent seeds of poesy [poetry]'. Folklore appears in the poem 'Halloween' and, of course, Tam o Shanter.

In 1789 the English artist and antiquarian Captain Francis Grose stayed with the Riddells at Friar's Carse near Dumfries where their next-door neighbour was Robert Burns. It seems that Burns and the antiquarian got on famously and in their ensuing discussion Burns suggested to the good Captain that when he was in Ayrshire, etching the castles there, that he do one of Kirk Alloway. One might imagine a lukewarm response, but Burns added that it was haunted and thereby captured the antiquarian's attention. Grose suggested that he would do the etching on condition that Burns produce a poem to go with it. A year later Burns got around to sending three folktales, one of which he might convert into a narrative poem. Grose chose the one that became Tam o Shanter. The original tale, it has been said, was heard by Burns when visiting Kenmure Castle, near Dalry in Galloway. The story seems authentic enough and there is a Dalry tale called Adam Forrester and the Circle of Steel (the tale can be found in my Folktales of Dumfries and Galloway) which, apart from the ending, parallels Burns's poem. However, there would have been a plethora of such tales heard in the cottages of the south-west. Here are the other two tales.

It was a stormy night, so wild that one might have thought the Devil had his hand in it. There were whirling squalls and bitter blasts of hail as a young farm-hand made his way back from the smithy to his farm, two plough-irons over his shoulder. As he approached the dark outlines of Kirk Alloway, a shudder of dread coursed through him. If the Earl of Hell was about, this deserted building was surely his haunt. As he drew closer, the lad saw, to his horror, that the windows were partly illuminated. Perhaps because of the few glasses of uisge-beatha he had enjoyed at the smithy, our foolhardy hero ventured a peek in the window. Luckily the temporary denizens had set off on some maleficent errand and the place was empty, except for a cauldron which hung from a roof beam over a fire. The lad entered and saw that the contents of the pot were the heads of unchristened babies, limbs of executed criminals and the like. He lifted down the pot and poured the unholy contents on the floor. He then upended it, put it over his shoulder and took it home where it served the family for many years and as living evidence of the truth of his tale.

The second tale Burns suggested was to become Tam o Shanter, but in his letter to Francis Grose he refers to him only as a Carrick farmer. In this prose piece there is no 'Weel done cutty sark!' but rather the line 'Well luppen [leaped] Maggy wi' the short sark.' Doesn't have quite the same ring about it. Lovers of this great poem might have noticed the reference in the tale above to unchristened bairns which Burns uses again in Tam o Shanter as being some of the items on the haly [holy] table. The folklore behind this is based on the belief that if a child died unchristened, they were either fated to roam the earth forever or become the property of Hell. Nice.

Now to Burns's other suggestion:

One summer's evening as the day expired a shepherd lad had put his ewes into the fold and was making his way home past Kirk Alloway. In the adjoining field a group of men and women were pulling up stems of the ragwort plant. Not in itself a strange thing, but the fact that they then sat astride them was. While this was a little strange, that is not what intrigued our sheepboy: it was the fact that, as each uttered the cry, 'Up Horsie', they shot into the air as if on Pegasus himself. Intrigued by this display the boy pulled up the plant, set himself astride it and uttered the cry. In an instant he was up and away. Grasping the flower tightly he scudded over hill and dale, through cloud and clear until he came to a vast broad land with warm scented air. No one told him, but he had been transported to the French region of Bordeaux. The others spiralled down, and he followed, arriving at a tavern. The crew, including the shepherd, were ushered into a wine cellar where a merry band of people were drinking glasses of claret. The drinking went on all night until just before dawn when the Ragwort Riders departed, before the sun interfered with their dark magic. Alas the poor shepherd laddie was a stranger to the land and to French wine and had succumbed to the alcohol. He was found later in the day by the wine merchant's staff. Fortunately, one had spent time in Scotland, so was able to converse with the boy and tell where he was. By means unknown to us, the young shepherd found his way back to Alloway and lived long to tell the world the wondrous tale.

17
The Cailleach

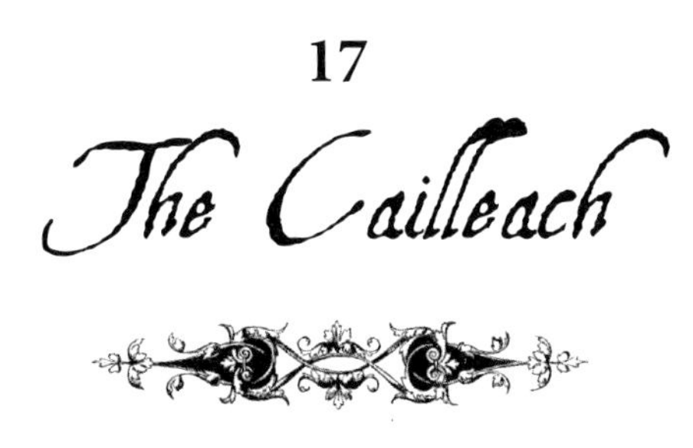

The Cailleach of Arran was fond of eating sailors - perhaps it was the salt that made them more tasty. To capture her prey, she would straddle the firth, one foot near Kilmory on Arran and one below Ballantrae in Carrick. Her preference was to drop a stone on the ship and sink it. She would then scoop the seamen out of the water. Once she saw a large French schooner coming up the North Channel from the Irish Sea and at the opportune moment stepped from Arran to Carrick. Unfortunately, the schooner had a particularly high mast which ran along the Caillach's nether regions. The ensuing tickle caused her to drop the stone, a particularly large one, and there it remains to this day: Ailsa Craig.

18
The Caird o' Barullion

The Laird of Bargally, a rather unpleasant bully of a man, was riding northwards down Glen Muck, a mile south of Dalmellington, when he was confronted by a man with a bandanna over his nose and mouth and a pistol. 'Yer pootch, sir!' commanded the assailant.

Now Bargally was a brave and resolute man, he was also not without some wisdom and decided he would lull the robber into a false sense of security. 'Better ma purse than ma life,' he said.

'Wysely spoken,' said the thief.

The laird unbuckled his purse and leaned over to hand it to the masked man when he drew back and made to strike with the pouch. It was a misjudged move, as the thief managed to grab the bag and haul it out of the laird's grip. The laird drew his sword and swung it at the highwayman's head. The man ducked causing his bonnet and wig to fly off and the bandanna to slip, momentarily revealing his face. Deciding that caution is preferable to rash bravery, the assailant took to his heels and up the steep slope of the glen. With the bandit now having the advantage of height and still with his gun, the laird also erred on the side of caution and rode on to Dalmellington to get help.

As the brigand headed off towards Bellsbank and the laird to Dalmellington, a farmer from Bantoberick made his way down the glen. Noticing the wig and bonnet and being without, stuck them on his head. Pleased with his new-found attire and sure his family would be impressed, he continued northwards. He had not gone but a few yards when a party of riders bore down on him; at the head of them was the Laird of Bargally. 'That's the man!' he cried, and the farmer was promptly tied up and dragged to Dalmellington, all the time protesting his treatment. On arrival at the clachan he discovered the reason for his arrest and truthfully said that he had found the wig and bonnet and knew nothing about a robbery. No one was listening.

After having been chained up for a week, the pathetic farmer was dragged before the judge of the Circuit Court. The laird and his fellow riders all bore witness that they had apprehended Bantoberick on the site of the robbery and that he still wore the same bonnet and wig as the laird had indicated during the actual robbery, though the purse and bandanna could not be found. The magistrate gave a baleful look to the prisoner and was about to pass judgment when a man stood up and marched up to the front of the court, lifted the wig and bonnet and plopped both on his head. After a brief adjustment to get it straight he looked at Bargally and said, 'Luik at me sir!' he commanded. 'Tell me on yer oath, am a no the man wha robbit ye?'

The laird looked hard at the man and truth dawned on him, 'By Heaven, this is the very man.'

The stranger turned to the judge, and with an air of exasperation, said, 'You see whit sort o memory the gentleman has, ma lord. He swears tae the bonnet whateer features are unner it. If ye were tae pit the bonnet an wig on yersel, nae dout he wuid swear ye were the verra man wha robbit him.'

For a moment the magistrate looked non-plussed. He then frowned, thought a bit then banged down his gavel, 'Case dismissit.' The stranger then turned to Bantoberick and winked before walking calmly to the door, leaving an open-mouthed and impotent Bargally to sit and fume.

The stranger was indeed the man who had robbed the laird in return for his mistreatment of travelling folk in Galloway. He was none other than William Marshall, the Caird, or Gypsy, of Barullion, or to give him his own title, 'King of the Gypsies of the Western Lowlands'.

In his life William (Billy) Marshall enlisted in the army seven times and deserted seven times, enlisted in the navy three times, deserting three times. He was lawfully married seventeen times and fathered four children after he was one hundred years old. He was lauded and loved and held sway over the Roma (Gypsy) folk of Carrick and Galloway. William was born in Kirkmichael, Ayrshire, around 1671, and died in Kirkcudbright. His grave in the old kirkyard states:

The Remains of
William Marshall
Tinker, who died
28th Novr, 1793
at the advanced age of
120 Years

If you should visit the grave, please leave a penny or two for any poor wayfarer who might follow.
Billy also appears in Sir Walter Scott's Guy Mannering.
Barullion/Barullion Fell is a set of hills in Wigtownshire; Bargally is just outside Newton Stewart.

19

Some Gaelic-speaking worthies from the hills of Carrick decided to visit their cousins in Gaeltachd of the Highlands of the north. The main purpose was to visit a place that was reported to have the most perfect echo. Many days riding later, they arrived deep in the Western Highlands and stayed overnight in a local hostelry. After enquiring of the landlord who could direct them to the aforementioned place, a local guide was found who was knowledgeable on the landscape and its histories. He, also mounted on a pony, led the way. After a journey of half an hour, they dismounted and climbed on to a rocky knoll that faced into a small secluded glen. Once everyone was there, the Gael, with great ceremony and pride, turned and in his best Gaelic called, 'Is there anybody there?' 'Is there anybody there?' came back instantly. The Highlander followed with, 'What is your name?' The same was heard. He turned to the Carrick folk, 'Would you like to have a try?'

One bold Southron stepped forward, and in his best Gallovidian Gaelic, said, 'It's lovely to be here.' This was repeated with perfection. The man smiled and turned to his wife, 'Would you like to have a go?'

The woman stepped forward, then turned to the group, 'Do you think it can speak French?' she said, with a knowing grin, 'Salutations à vous,' she called, in her best Parisian French. The echo replied.

The group laughed, and another gentleman stepped forward. 'Perhaps some Portuguese might go down well. 'Saudações de Portugal.' He called into the distance and Portuguese filled the air in response. The Carrick folk clapped with delight. The Highlander stood, his jaw dropped and his face a picture of amazement, 'I find this very strange, for I come here at least once a week and I know for certain that the strange creature that replies has always been here and certainly has never been abroad. So, it is a puzzle to me where it has learned these foreign tongues.'

The Carrickach were too polite to laugh, though a few did express their mirth through discreet coughs.

20

Cormack MacNiall and the Mermaid

Cormack MacNiall was a young fisherman and sometime smuggler of Lendalfoot. Each day he would row out into the firth and drop his creels, then tow his longline gently towards Girvan or Ballantrae, according to the winds. Sometimes he could be found - though preferably not - taking kegs of whisky to an Isle of Man brig and returning with spices and sugar from the Indies The only days he did not go out was when storms were due or the thin wind from the east blew hard. Not only did it cut through the best of garments, it also blew him away towards Ailsa Craig, and that was ten miles out. When fishing, he would rise before dawn and be heading out before the sun appeared. When he was not fishing, he would tend the small croft up Lendal Water. His house was a small self-built butt and ben.

One morning in the summer of 1668, as he walked shorewards, he saw a strange shape on the rocks near where he kept his boat. There was just enough light to see that it seemed human, but it was only as he reached the boat that he saw it was a mermaid. Cormack certainly believed that they existed and had heard tales of encounters, but he had never seen one until now. Unsure what to do he untied the vessel from the rocks and began pushing it towards the water. 'Good morning Cormack MacNiall,' she said, as she brushed her long hair.

He was startled to hear him called by his name and stuttered, 'Eh…eh… guid mornin.'

'I think you will have a good morning's fishing; the wind is in your favour.' Her voice had a soft gentle tone, much like a Gaelic speaker.

'Thank ye,' he said automatically, then recovering himself from his wonderment, said, 'Ye ken me?'

'We know everyone who fishes our waters.'

There was no threat in her voice but it unsettled Cormack, as if he was a trespasser, allowed only to ply his trade by favour of the sea people. 'Where is your home?' he asked, out of natural curiosity.

'We live in a great grotto just beyond the island you call Ailsay. My father is king of the ocean as far as you can see and beyond. You live in a butt and ben up the Lendal Water; it is pretty, but very small.'

'A biggit it masel,' he said, a little peeved at her description, 'it's muckle eneuch fer me.'

'Is it? She raised an eyebrow, 'A man of your mettle cannot be satisfied with a mere hovel.'

'No ainly is it smaa, nou it's a hovel.'

'I don't mean to be harsh, but your family were well enough off.'

The use of 'were' stung him more than the seeming insults about his house. 'Aye, bit ma faither lost it aa then killt hissel. That killt ma mither an left me an ma brither wi nocht. Aa a hae, I hae makit masel.

'Come back here at this time tomorrow and I will help you a little.' Before Cormack could ask her name, she rolled off the rock into a pool and swam away into the incoming tide.

The young man stood and watched her seemingly melt into the water, intrigued at what the help might be; then, with a shrug, he pushed the boat into the water, leaped aboard and went fishing.

That night he had trouble sleeping. He could not rest his mind as he went over and over again his strange encounter. She was half fish, half woman, with seaweed coloured hair and green-tinged skin. Her lips were the colour of coral and, though he knew it would be wrong, he longed to see her again and to kiss them; it was more than just curiosity.

Morning came and he made his way to the beach just before the dawn. She was already there brushing out the wetness from her long locks of hair. 'Good morning Cormack. How are you today?'

'A'm weel. Hou's yersel?'

'I am well, thank you.' She looked out across the cold, grey breakers to the mist-shrouded sea, 'It is so beautiful,' she said.

'A'm nae sae suir o the beauty on a cauld, greyday lik the day.'

'Every day you are alive is beautiful, you just need to find the beauty in it.'

'But grey is no exactly whit ye wuid caa a bonnie colour.'

'Grey granite, a gathering storm, the bark on a tree: are these not beautiful?

'Aye, a see whit ye mean.' He gave a short laugh and felt a surge of love for her.

The mermaid seemed to sense this and opened her hand to reveal a diamond encrusted ring, 'In this light it is grey; is it not beautiful?

Cormack's eyes widened, 'That is bonnie, bonnie lass.'

She held it towards him, 'It is yours, if you wish.'

He felt an irresistible urge to possess it and almost grabbed it from her hand, 'Is this fer me?'

'Only if you want it.'

'Dinnae ye want it?'

'We see no real beauty in these things. They are pretty enough; but beauty for us is in the changing moods of the ocean, the rising and the setting sun or the stars that roof the world. But the greatest beauty is in the love of family and friends. That serves our commonwealth. You people of the land seem to value these trinkets above all. You steal, you kill, you enslave each other to gather these things.'

'No everyane. As a fisherman a hae watchit and loed the simmer sundoun ower Arran. A ken the beauty o storms. Bit forby a ken their savagery an hae lost mony a freen tae the moods o the ocean. Oor warld is basit on exchange o guids and if a hae muckle then a spen it in ma community. Wealth can serve the common guid.'

'I understand. But there is also excessive wealth and greed and abject poverty. That does not exist with us. Everyone's belly has enough.'

'Whaur is the ring frae?' he asked.

'The bottom of the sea is littered with the wrecks of ships full of people craving wealth and dying in the process.'

Cormack almost blurted out, 'Really?' but restrained himself. 'That's sad,' he said, meaning it, but intrigued by the idea of wrecks full of treasure.

'They and their contents are of no interest to us except that sometimes they endanger our homes.'

They talked together until late morning then Cormack launched his boat and together, she swimming, they travelled into the deep. Half a mile out he turned southwards, and she continued west, 'Will I see you tomorrow?' she called back.

'Aye!'

The following day, though she waited until noon, Cormack did not appear, nor the next. He appeared the day after; as he approached, he noticed she was slightly crestfallen, 'You said you would come two days ago.'

'A'm sairry, bit I hud tae gang tae Girvan on business, an wis detained a wee.' He hoped she could not read his face too well as he was not entirely truthful, having gone to sell the ring.

'Do you not want to see me?'

'Yes, of course.' He gave a short nervous laugh, afraid that he had soured their relationship.

'I brought you more,' she said, holding up a small chest. She opened it revealing rubies, emeralds and diamonds. Her voice seemed to have a level of desperation and he did not miss it.

'Thank you,' he said, almost half-heartedly, and laid it down in the sand as if unimpressed.

'You don't like them?' she said, her previous commanding-self disappearing in self-doubt.

'They're lovely, but I thought if there's so much treasure down there perhaps a big chest would be better. Just think of the help to my community.' He tried to be sincere, but the thought of great wealth was too much. She turned her head away and looked out to Ailsay. Cormack did not notice her eyes harden

'Come tomorrow and I will give you all the wealth you can imagine.'

He laughed with a near hysterical joy, 'I can imaigine a hantle.'

'I'm sure you can,' she said, slipping off the rock and leaving without a farewell.

Cormack abandoned his boat and walked away up the Lendal, the small box of precious stones under his arm. It was a laird's ransom and soon a laird he would be. The excitement was almost crippling; his mind was in a frenzy of ideas: acres of land, a great mansion, horses and carriages, servants and the choice of any girl around. The journey through to the following morning was torturous, but eventually it came. He decided to keep her waiting a little so as not to seem over keen. When he did arrive at the shore the mermaid was not there. It was like a stab to the groin. He frantically looked about and then noticed that his boat was missing: a double blow. What now? Just as disappointment was creeping up on him, he saw a speck out on the water. It was a boat with someone aboard, and though there was no sign of rowing, the boat made good speed across the waves. Two-hundred yards out he saw that it was his own craft with the mermaid aboard. Excitement made him giddy, 'As she neared the shore he called out, 'I thocht…och, neer mind, it is guid tae see ye.'

'I'm sure it is,' she said, a coldness in her voice and a smile that did not reach her eyes, 'Climb aboard.'

The fisherman leaped on to his craft and sat facing the maid, his face a great joyous mass of smiles. The boat turned about of its own volition and headed rapidly out to sea; faster and faster it sped along, bouncing off the wavetops and slapping down hard in the troughs. It was thrilling and frightening at the same time. The mermaid's face was impassive as she looked past Cormack to the great mass of Ailsay as it loomed higher and higher. When they reached the great craig, the boat slowed and cruised to the far side. The air was full of the wash of waves on the rock and the cry of seabirds from above. As they rounded to the west side Cormack saw a cave appear. The boat sailed straight into the narrow entrance and beached on a bank of sand. Stacked against the wall were piles of chests, some open, with crowns, tiaras, necklaces, bracelets and precious stones cascading out of them. Even in his wildest imagination Cormack could not believe what he saw. Never mind a few acres of land; with this he could buy a kingdom. He could feel his heart beating hard against his ribcage at the vastness of his new-found wealth. Without so much as a look at the mermaid he jumped from the boat and grabbed handfuls of jewels. He gave a great whoop before turning to the fish-woman who had given him treasure beyond imagination. In one hand she held a wine-bottle and in the other two goblets, 'Shall we drink to your great fortune?'

'Aye,' he said, taking a vessel from her hand.

She poured ruby-red liquid into it until full and some into her own, 'To your prosperity,' she said.

'Tae ma prosperity,' he said and gulped down the drink, 'Hah!' he said with a great flourish of wiping his mouth on his sleeve. She raised her goblet and put it to her lips. Cormack looked deep into her eyes which grew cold then distant then hazy; he was overcome with an overpowering urge to sleep.

Cormack McNiall raised himself from the floor of the cave, stretched and yawned, 'I must have fallen asleep,' he said, then stared non-plussed at the figure in the boat which now floated near the mouth of the cave.

'I loved you Cormack and thought that you loved me; but like most people of the land you are tied to wealth and greed and possessions. Well now you *are* tied to it and will be forever.' The boat sailed out of the cave and out of sight. The fisherman rose from the sand and made towards the treasure, but as he reached out for it his hand stopped short, as did his other. Looking at his wrists he saw he was manacled to the wall, his fingers just inches away from his riches. Close, but so far away. He sank to his knees in anguish and howled in hopelessness.

It is said that if you pass Ailsay on certain days, when the wind is in the east, the light is fading and the first stars shine above, then you can hear those anguished cries above the sound of Cormack MacNiall's chains.

21

The past is a foreign country: they do things differently there.
L.P. Hartley: The Go-Between

In these, allegedly, more compassionate times, we condemn or revise the use of certain words, considering them inappropriate or insensitive. But that is the nature of language: meaning or use changes and can turn a word into something hurtful, especially when used as unfeeling slang. It goes the other way too. The word nice, on its journey from the Latin nescius, meaning ignorant, to its present usage, meant to act like a simpleton - the last word now being inappropriate. The word daft used to mean gentle or meek and in Scots it was used to denote a person who was merry and playful. Now on with our wee simple story:

Daft Jock Aird was born in Kirkmichael and was buried, after seventy-nine years, in the graveyard at Dalrymple. Jock was not a tall man. In fact, he was rather small. But what he lacked in height he gained in personality, and in that he was a giant; and for that he was held in great affection. When he entered a village, the word would go out and people would come to hail his arrival and departure, especially the children. To add to his demeanour, Jock carried a stout walking stick, and as he arrived, he would carry a haughty air of indifference; in truth, he was keeping an eye out for mischief. Often the young people would, as was their wont at that time, to chant rude rhymes as he passed; sometimes including Jock in the text. At this he would put on an air of silent contempt until one of the perpetrators got up close and personal. At this Jock would spin about and his walking stick would become a weapon of revenge and punishment. One such day as he passed through Ochiltree he had just administered a suitable 'thwack' to an over-stepping lad and took on an air of victory. The local minister seeing this, called out, 'Dear me, John; you seem to be walking on air.'

Jock gave him a respectful nod, 'Naw meenister, ye are wrang, a'm walkin on Ochiltree.'

22

Donald of Dundonald

Between Troon and Kilmarnock lies the large village of Dundonald. In Gaelic the word *Dun* means a fortification, and in the case of Dundonald, refers to the castle that sits on a motted hill. The site has long been fortified, probably from pre-history. It was a fort in the Iron Age then a motte and bailey, probably with a wooden fortification. The first stone building was erected by Alexander Stewart in the 1200s. The present building, though somewhat depleted, was built by Robert Stewart around 1371 on his accession to the crown of Scotland as Robert II. So why is it called Dundonald and not Dunrobert? Well it seems that long ago, before the Stewarts, there lived atop the hill a certain Donald. All that remained of any fortification was a large monolith around which Donald had planted columbine and honeysuckle. He loved nothing more than to sit in the scented air of his wee garden and watch the sun set over Arran. One day, to his dismay, he saw his neighbour planting trees. This was an excellent idea, as the landscape had been long denuded and timber was in short supply. What troubled our hero was that he presumed that the trees would grow rapidly up to a height that would obscure his beloved panorama. He relayed his fears to his wife Meg, who wasn't altogether sympathetic 'It's aboot time we had some decent wuid tae burn. I'm seek o burnin peat. Aa a can keuk is parritch an stew. A pickle roast venison wuid gang doon a treat.'

'Aye weel ye maun get yer wuid, bit a'm gaun tae big a caustle heigh eneuch tae luik ower it aa.'

'An whaur will ye get the siller tae big a caustle?'

'A hud a dream that a traivelit tae Lunnon and in the mid o Lunnon Brig I fand a bag o gowd.'

His wife nodded her head and raised her brows, 'So ye're aff tae Lunnon tae pick up the gowd?

'Aye!'

'Yer an eediot!'

'Hou?'

'There's hunners o fowk in Lunnon and dizzens crossin ower the brig. Dae ye think they'll juist ignore the bag o gowd acause ye're cumin doon fae Scotland?'

'Aye!'

'Ye're a dooble eediot!'

With a bag of oats, salt and a thin flat stone as a cooking girdle on his back, our hero headed south.

'Donald!' his wife, tears in her eyes, called after him, 'Tak tent, ye auld eediot.'

He took off his bonnet and waved, just before he disappeared out of sight.

The journey took all of three weeks to reach the wall that surrounded the city. After some difficulty with the local dialect he was directed to the aptly named Cripplegate - his legs were worn and weary. It took him, after a few zig-zags, another half hour to reach the bridge. He had never seen anything quite like it: there was a series of twenty pontoons from which stretched stone arches. All along the bridge were multi-storey buildings, their main structure built above the pontoons. In the middle was a drawbridge to allow high-masted boats to pass. Donald reasoned that his bag of gold would be at this point. As he made his way across the bridge his excitement grew until he was almost shaking with delight, 'Och if Meg cuid anely see this. Dizzens o folk? There's hunners, an aa walkin past ma bag o gowd. When he reached the massive drawbridge, his head was giddy with expectation. There was nothing on the bridge, but it could be at either end or maybe hanging from the side - perhaps a passing boat had snagged it, or a thief had stashed it away. Donald scoured the area, even, to the curiosity of passers-by, climbing over the side to inspect beneath. Nothing. As he clambered back on to the walkway he was distraught. 'Fower hunner mile fer nuthin. Meg wis richt, A am an eediot. Och! I cannae gang back hame: the shame o it. A'll juist haftae dae awa wi masel.' In a state of complete dejection, he climbed on to the parapet in preparation for his demise. A'll coont tae three then fling masel aff.' Donald began to swing his arms, 'Yin, twa…'

'Oi!' came a voice from behind, and hand grabbed the back of his coat, 'Wot you doin?'

Donald was unceremoniously hauled from his perch down onto the walkway of the drawbridge. He sat for a moment, his head in chaos, looking up at his assailant, for he was not the least bit thankful for his rescue. 'A…A wis trying tae fling masel in the river.'

'Wot? Was you tryin to kill yourself?'

Donald understood the question, though the dialect was very foreign. He nodded.

'Why?'

He replied slowly hoping the Londoner would understand Scots, 'I cam … I cam,' he pointed away with his right index finger, 'frae Scotland.'

The man nodded, 'Yes.'

'A dream', Donald made a sleeping gesture, 'Here a bag o gowd, gowd … gold.'

The man burst into laughter, 'Funny,' he said, which unsettled the Scotsman: he was not fond of being made a fool of.

'It's no funny,' said Donald, doubly peeved. He shook his head.

The man nodded, 'I had the same dream, except I was on top of a hill with a big stone covered in flowers.' He gestured to emphasise, 'I dug a hole and found a bag of gold. Gowd.' He laughed again, 'Funny, innit?'

Donald followed most of what the stranger had said, enough to get the gist of it. He made a winding gesture with his finger, 'Again.' The man repeated what he had said, this time slower while Donald repeated the words. Now he knew exactly what the man was saying and laughed fit to burst.

After a flagon of ale, Donald bid farewell to his new friend, made his way out of London and up the Great North Road for Scotland. He made the journey in ten days. The first thing he did was give his wife the hug of her life, 'Cam wi me, a need ma paidle.' he said, then made for his tool store. Meg followed. He took out the spade and walked over to the standing stone. The honeysuckle never smelt sweeter as he dug. A few holes later he, literally, hit gold. As he threw out the coins at his wife's feet, she danced a jig of joy. Donald took a momentary break and turned to Meg, 'Are ye gled ye be mairryit tae an eediot?'

Meg threw her arms about her husband 'Taks wan tae ken wan.'

And so, Donald built his castle and all about named it Donald's fort or … Dundonald.

Note: In folklore this is deemed Type 1645: Rich through a Dream, and can be found all across Europe and the Middle East. The most famous English version is the Peddlar of Swaffham. It's also found in Arabian Night's Tales or 1001 Nights.

23

Dreep frae the Thack

A shepherd had taken charge of a moorland out by Muirkirk and set out with his wife, two sons and three daughters and all their possessions. It was their intention to build a new onstead with house, barns and pens on the moor. After a day of investigation, they found a suitable site with a spring and plenty of good stone for the walls of the buildings. Heather was in abundance for thatch. First, they set up a temporary home with bent hazel sticks and canvas. Using their horse and cart they began the hard work of hauling boulders and stones to the site. A large, three-feet-wide rectangular trench was then dug and then two rows of the first large foundation boulders rolled into place parallel to each other. The space between would be filled with turf to stop the wind and for insulation. Half-way through the morning and on completion of the south facing wall with space for a door, the family sat down to enjoy a large plate of porridge. As they sat along the foundations eating silently, a group of small people emerged out of the heather. They were an exact copy of the shepherd's family; except they were half the height. The shepherd, though a little taken aback, hailed them merrily, 'Guid mornin tae ye. Are ye oot fer a wee walk?'

'Naw, we leeve here,' said the wee man.

The shepherd looked about, 'An whaur wid that be?'

'Richt here,' said the wee wife. The wee children nodded.

The shepherd gave his head a shake and looked about, 'But there's naethin here.'

'Aye there is,' insisted the wee man. There's oor hoose and ye are biggin yer hoose near on tap o it. When we hae an onding, the dreep fae yer thack will faa exactly doon oor lum.'

It was then that the shepherd and his wife realised that they had neighbours. Not just any neighbours but Good Neighbours, the fairy folk.

Unwilling to upset these good folks, the shepherd moved the house fifty yards away, which pleased their neighbours greatly.

24
The Enchanted Saddle

Sir Fergus Barclay was a real person. He was the Laird of Ardrossan and lived at Ardrossan Castle. Some of the stories in this book attributed to Michael Scott are elsewhere attributed to Sir Fergus. He has also been blessed, or cursed, with the epithet, Deil o Ardrossan.

They say, 'If ye sup wi the deil, ye maun sup wi a lang spuin'. Another is, 'Be carefu o whit ye wish fer. For Sir Fergus Barclay of Ardrossan both applied. He saw the wealth of others around him, but he 'always seemed doomed to penury'. He never thought it was his fault, always someone else's. The fact that he preferred to idle his time and gamble what little he had did not occur to him as contributing to his misfortune. Like people of that ilk, he wanted an easy solution. What he did not know was that being beholden to the Devil did not necessarily mean swearing an oath; sometimes wishful thinking could be enough. It was after a particularly bad round of cards that he made his mistake. 'If anely I had the Deil's luck,' he muttered as he rode home to Ardrossan Castle. As he made his way, a horse came cantering up from behind, slowing as it approached. Fergus's hand automatically went to the hilt of his sword. The stranger was mounted on a jet-black horse with an ornate saddle of finest embossed leather with silver edging. Even the stirrups seemed of silver and were heavily engraved. His clothes were of the finest black gabardine and of a military cut. The ensemble was finished off with a high-collared cape and a broad-brimmed hat. The face had a darker complexion, not unlike the Spanish soldiers he had encountered in the European wars, and the stranger's thin, well-groomed moustache was decidedly European. What intrigued Fergus was that he could not guess the age of the man. He had the bearing of someone who had lived a full life, had wisdom, cunning and carried an air of supreme self-assurance, yet had an almost youthful appearance. 'Good day, sir, do you ride far?' he said.

Fergus, always wary of the motives of others, said, 'Far eneuch.'

The stranger gave a short laugh. 'Far enough. Fair enough. I just thought if we were going the same way we could share a little company.'

'Ardrossan,' said Fergus.

'I'm sorry?'

'A'm gaun tae Ardrossan.'

'I do not know this place. I am from very far south on my way to the far north, you might say. And you know, it is killing me. The horse is a fine horse but occasionally has a mind of its own and the saddle is beyond unbearable. My tender behind is black and blue. How is your horse?'

'The nag is braw, has a guid pace, rides weel and the saddle is perfit. It haes been weel-ileit an luikit-efter fer mony years.'

'Mm!' said the stranger, approvingly, 'Perhaps we should exchange.'

Fergus looked at the horse and saddle, 'I cuid dae that,' he said, in his best ingenuous voice.

'Hah!' laughed the stranger, 'with respect, my dear friend, I was jesting. This is an Arab thoroughbred. I could exchange him alone for a hundred of your beasts, good as they might seem. The saddle is tooled Spanish leather with the finest silver inlay. The metal of the stirrups is Toledo steel that has been tempered until is unbreakable and will not tarnish with the rain. When I obtained the saddle, I was told that a witch had praised it, declaring that whoever rode it would always experience success, and I certainly have had that. But thank-you for your offer.'

On they rode getting friendlier by the mile. Fergus learned little of the stranger, for he, dominated the conversation, telling of his worries and woes: of the loss of his beloved wife at the birth of his son and of the less-loved, second wife he had married to care for his son and who had herself the temerity to give birth to a daughter.

They arrived at Ardrossan and Fergus offered the stranger a bed for the night, which he gladly accepted, complaining of tiredness and a very sore bottom. In the morning, at a breakfast of porridge and wild blaeberries the stranger, who gave his name as Don Huerco, once again complained of the pain in his rear, 'I was thinking, my dear friend, of a bargain we could strike that would suit both of us.'

Fergus looked at the Spaniard with interest, 'An that is?'

'That I leave my horse and saddle with you, and in temporary exchange I take your horse and saddle.'

Fergus nodded approvingly. 'That is guidwillt, an a bargain, a wuid be blythe tae accept.

'There is just one other thing, not that I mistrust you, but the world sometimes changes rapidly, and I need to preserve my property. All I wish is that you sign a document to say that you are in my debt until you return to me the Arab stallion, El Noche, and his saddle. I have prepared the document already, feeling that you would assent to the bargain.'

Fergus read the document, which also had a superb drawing of the horse and saddle, and an end note that, should Don Huerco not return within five years, the horse would be the property of Sir Fergus. 'Five years?' he inquired.

'Yes, the business will probably take up to that time.'

Fergus smiled, realising he had the better side of the bargain by a long chalk. A little later he bid farewell to Don Huerco, hoping secretly he would never see him again, and went into the stable to enjoy his new, and hopefully permanent, possession.

First thing he did was to set about breeding from the stallion, he also took it on jaunts to the continent where everyone admired the magnificent beast and its equally magnificent saddle. While abroad Sir Fergus continued his gambling with vigour and endlessly won until his fortune was great. At home his stable-hands were raising and training the Arab crosses who proved to be faster than any of the horses in Cunningham except, of course, El Noche. One two-year old, who had the colouring and the temperament of his father, was the fastest horse for a hundred miles and young Barclay had a hankering to ride him; but his father would not let him near the animal until he was a sufficiently skilled rider. It was at this time that Sir Fergus went out alone to hunt deer. Thinking it better to hunt on foot among the trees, he hobbled Don Huerca's horse in a clearing and set out, bow and arrow at the ready. After an hour he managed to down a young buck and returned to collect the horse only to find it gone and the untied hobble discarded in the grass. He walked home in a fury, swearing revenge on the culprit. The perpetrator was never found, and it was from this day that Barclay's luck changed. The first sign was losing at gambling, then other little tragedies began to manifest themselves on him. The worst was yet to come.

Sir Fergus had business in Edinburgh and was set to be away for over a week. The son took the opportunity to command the stable-hands to get the skittish, black horse ready. Their protests were met with threats, that as he was master of the castle while his father was away, they would do his bidding or lose their jobs. Saddled up, the boy set out across the moors, thrilled to be on such an elegant animal. It effortlessly strode the miles, leaping dykes and burns with grace. As they turned and began the race for home, they encountered a wide stream with deep banks. The horse, seeing the obstacle at the last minute, swerved and sent the youth flying over its shoulder. His head struck a rock killing him instantly. His body was not found until the very day of his father's return. On seeing the broken body of his son and heir, Barclay flew into an unstoppable rage, vented his spleen on his innocent wife and killed her with a single blow of his fist to her head. When the rage settled, he realised the gravity of his crime and fled, taking most of his gold and silver and leaving his daughter to fend for herself. Secretly, he took a boat to Arran and found his way south to Kildonan where he lived the life of a hermit in a stone tower, with only a servant for company. For years his days were spent in gloomy isolation looking out to the distant crags of Ailsey. On one cold morning he and his servant set out to gather driftwood for the fire when they passed an aged woman leaning upon a stick. As they drew alongside, she raised the staff and pointed it at the knight, her steely eyes looking deep into him, 'Sir Fergus Barclay, wuid ye be sae kind as tae lay a siller coin on the palm o ma haun and a wull tell whit lies aheid o ye.' Barclay's first instinct was to take the stick and thrash her for impudence, but his curiosity got the better of him. He opened his pouch, pulled out a small silver coin and placed it on her open palm. She clasped the money, placed her fist on the side of her head and screwed up her face. She stood like that for ten seconds then deftly deposited the coin in her purse. 'Ye must neer put a fuit on Erse soil. Gin ye dae, ye'll dee.'

'A hae nae intention o veesitin or een settin fuit on Erin. Aff ye gang, ye auld rascal, afore a tak yer stick an thresh ye or pit ma fuit in yer erse.'

She gave him a fierce look, 'A hae said whit a hae said. Dinnae tread on Erse soil,' she said, then continued on her way.

Later in the month, while out foraging alone on the seashore, Fergus saw a large boat unloading turf and laying it out to dry above the tideline. The crew completed their work and the boat set sail southwards towards Ailsey. Fergus continued his search gathering shellfish and seaweed. Out of curiosity he wandered up to the turf, walking over it and guessing it had been placed there to be used to cover a roof on a cottage that was being built nearby. After collecting a fair amount of seafood, he walked back to his tower and bade his servant prepare supper. As he sat eating a long trail of seaweed, he said to his retainer, 'A saw a boat drappin aff turf earlier the day.'

'Aye,' said the servant, 'it's an Erse boat. It's guid turf they bring.'

Fergus dropped the food back on the plate and placed his left hand over his mouth; he knew now his time had come. In a matter of days Fergus was fatally ill and died. Before his demise he ordered his man to sew him in a bullock skin and set him adrift on the firth. With a heavy heart the faithful agent did as he was bid, then dragged the encased body into the water just after high tide. The lowering sea took the body away. The tear-faced servant watched as a south-westerly breeze pushed the strange parcel towards Ayrshire. A week later it washed up in South Bay beneath the walls of Ardrossan Castle. Two women found the body and raised the alarm. With dignity and an undeserved reverence Sir Fergus's daughter had the body taken to the Barclay chapel and buried with due ceremony.

In the months and years that followed, a legend grew up around Sir Fergus, his horse and the saddle. That it was gift from the Devil and at a price. Be that as it may, there is one other strange aspect: though the name for the Devil in Spanish is *El Diablo*, he has a lesser known name: El Huerca.

Huerca in Spanish means horn and is a cousin to the old Scottish name for the Devil, Auld Hornie – see Francisco Goya's Witches' Sabbath (Prado Museum, Madrid).

25 Flaught o Fire

A man by the name of Brown was out on Dunlop Hill taking his usual morning constitutional walk when, much to his obvious surprise, a headless horse began to gallop round and round about him. Aware that the apparition was none other than the Great Beast himself in another horrifying disguise, the terrified man dropped to his knees and wailed, 'Dear God preserve this worthless sinner from the ravages of Satan,' At which point the Devil shot off in a flaught o fire.

Another family from Dunlop by the name of Craig had a reputation for being highly intelligent and of dabbling in the dark arts. The main source of evidence was an elderly lady who had entered their house while the family were at church. She had gone into their small sitting room and found books that were 'fu o kittle leukin Deil's figores an twirlie-whorlies'. Seeing these, she informed her neighbours that the family owned books on sorcery and magic. The books were in fact on arithmetic, algebra and geometry.

26 Hare Raising

The Cumnock area, like all places in Scotland, had its fair share of tales of witches, intent on mischief on man and beast. So much so that people were genuinely intimidated by anyone suspected of such alleged practices. A local woman by the name of Nannie Reid was particularly feared. She was rumoured to be able to adversely affect the milking of cows, the laying of eggs and even the baking of scones. To counter this people made sure that Nannie always had money, food and various gifts as a propitiation – a kind of supernatural protection racket.

It so happened that a young lad from Lowes farm at New Cumnock was out shooting on a fine spring morning. On seeing a hare, he raised the shotgun and fired. In an instant the hare popped on to its hind legs and began waving its forepaws, as if to say, 'Stop! Don't shoot!' The boy took fright and ran for home where he relayed the story to his mother. She, like the boy, though he had quite forgotten, knew that witches change into hares and have their sabbats out on the moors, most especially in early spring when the weather is more agreeable. With this in mind, she took him to a local wise woman. The woman listened to his tale, 'Aye, it is likely Nannie Reid or wan o her freens ye hae shotten,' she said.

The boy reacted in horror, 'Whit wull a dae? She'll turn me intae an esk or a puddock.'

The woman looked at the boy and raised an eyebrow, 'She micht; exceptin ye dae whit a tell ye: get a wee bit siller as'll fit in the barrel o yer gun, gang back tae whaur ye shot, an fire again. This suid dispel ony cantrip she micht lay on ye.'

The boy did as he was commanded, and no harm came to him.

The other thing the young lad possibly didn't know was that hares gather in groups on the moor in the spring mating season, rise on their hind legs and box each other.

27

Tam Tyler the chapman had spent the last forty years chapping on doors selling his wares; but times were hard and more and more doors were getting slammed in his face. Tam had never been wasteful with his earnings and had saved a not-inconsiderable amount of money. It was time to consider a change of occupation. While passing through Galston, or, as it's known locally, Gauston, he stopped at the local hostelry to 'wat his drouth'. In conversation with a couple of old acquaintances who were farmers, Tam bewailed his misfortune, 'A'm seek o bein a chapman. Naebody wants naethin nooadays. I want an easier job, like bein a fermer.'

The farmers looked at each other and one gave a brief nod then turned to Tam. 'Aye it's a cushy life bein a fermer. Naethin much tae dae aa day cept let the animals dae the wark an the corn grows itssel.' He narrowed his eyes and nodded at Tam. 'A'm thinkin o retiring tae gang an leeve wae ma dochter in Amerikay. Wuid ye be interestit in buyin ma ferm?'

Tam's natural business caution came into play, 'A'm no shuir. It wuid depend on the price.'

The farmer nodded, 'Of coorse. A'm no a greedy man, but a must hae a fair price.'

Tam nodded, 'Aye! Whit wuid ye be askin?'

'A thocht that a shillin a heid for aa ma beasts and ye can hae the lan an the hoose forby.'

Tam did a rough calculation of the cost and nearly blurted out his acceptance. Again, his natural business brain prevailed. He shook his head momentarily, put his hand to his chin as if deep in thought then, as if reluctant, said, 'Ye drive a hard bargain, but aye it's agreed. But we'll need tae get a legal bill drawn up.'

'Aye!' agreed the farmer.

As luck would have it, the local solicitor was having a dram with colleagues at the other end of the bar. The farmer called him over and with a sly wink explained the agreement. The solicitor nodded seriously and drew a sheet of parchment from his satchel along with a quill and inkhorn. Deftly he wrote out the agreement in a neat copperplate script and presented it to the farmer who duly signed. Tam followed suit and the other farmer witnessed the document. The farmer then bought a round of drinks before they all trooped out and headed towards Tam's new acquisition. The group walked round the farm counting out the fourteen cows, one bull, twenty-four ewes and two rams, a dozen hens and one cockerel, two collie dogs, three cats and a single sow. The total coming to sixty shillings or three pounds exactly. Tam was ecstatic: an entire farm for three pounds. He almost danced on the spot as he pulled the notes from his spleuchan. The farmer went to accept it but stopped short of touching the note. 'Och! He exclaimed. 'A forgot, there's a pickle mair beasties at the back o the byre.' They followed the farmer round the building and stopped at a row of a score of beehives. 'Noo let's see,' said the farmer, 'Three hunner bees a hive, times twinty, maks sax thoosan, plus the ither beasts comes tae three hunner an three poonds.'

Tam stood for a moment dumbstruck, then protested, 'Ye cannae coont the bees. A mean...'

The solicitor interjected, 'It's in the bill that ye signed Tam, a shillin a heid.'

'Aw!' wailed Tam in despair, 'A've no got that kina cash. Will ye tak a poond note in compenseetion, an ye can keep the ferm?'

The farmer took the note, 'That'll dae fine Tam. Whit'll ye dae noo?'

'A juist rememberit, A hae tae gang an see a freen ower in Cunninghame. A better awa.' With that Tam fled the scene leaving a trio of highly amused Kyloes.

It was months before Tam ventured back to Galston. When there, he was invited back to the farm for a dram and a bed for the night. He was also given a dozen jars of best honey for his troubles and another dozen each time he passed. Eventually Tam made a good profit from the bees and whiles about told the tale of how he had been teased and tricked by a wily farmer. It was sad day when the farmer eventually retired and moved away to live with his daughter ... in Kilmarnock.

28

An Ayrshire carter or carrier used to travel the roads of the county with his large cart and team of two shire horses. His main job was moving heavy goods such as furniture or barrels of beer and wine. As well as the heavy goods he also had a chest for carrying small, valuable items. For a companion he had a mastiff dog who had the habit of lagging to sniff out the occasional rabbit burrow. He was travelling south from Glasgow and was on the Fenwick moor as the sun set. Gradually the light faded, and he cursed the hold-up at the Broomilaw that made him late. It was the night of the full moon, but for the moment there was only deepening shadows. He peered ahead and thought he saw some movement. As he strained to see, out of the darkness, a man with a cudgel leaped up beside him and dragged him off the cart onto the ground. He was joined by another cudgel-wielding accomplice. 'Gie us the key tae yer strangbox or we'll theek ye,' said the first robber

The carter's response was to call loudly, 'Help! Help!'

'Hah! That'll dae ye nae guid,' said one of his assailants as he slapped him with the back of his left hand.

'Again, the carter called, 'Help.'

The thug slapped him again, 'A telt ye,

there's naebody aboot fer miles.' He lifted his hand to hit again when a mass of fury tore into him. The mastiff grabbed the man's forearm and sunk his teeth deep into the muscle; the would-be thief screamed in pain. Taking advantage of the diversion, the carter grabbed the man's dropped cudgel and laid into his companion, giving him a severe thrashing and sending him running across the moor. The carter then pulled his dog off the other and gave him a blow to the side of the head. 'Get!' he roared. The man didn't take a second telling and was off into the darkness. The carter kneeled, gave the dog a hug then patted its head and said, 'Good boy, Help.'

29

Hilloa for Cantyre

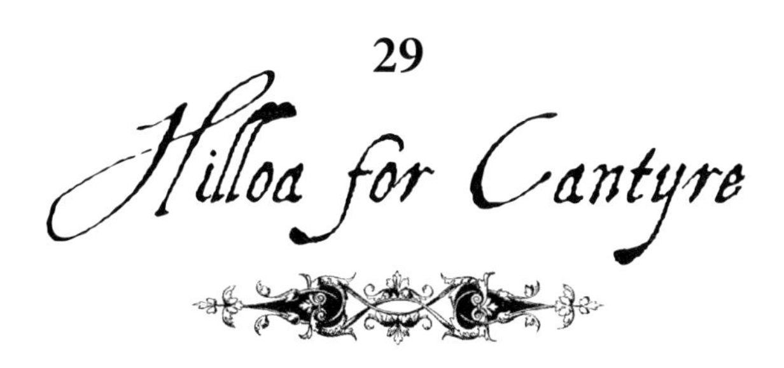

Young Jock was trekking toward Largs from Skelmorlie to buy a plank of wood and a rope for his boat. It was the thirty-first of October in the year 1599 and he was late on the road. Just as he was approaching the Routen Burn, he noticed the light of a fire flickering in a derelict cottage. As the wind had picked up and a light rain had begun to fall, he decided to seek shelter. The building was without doors, windows or a roof, but Jock thought it would provide some refuge. He peeked in the window and saw, to his puzzlement, a woman stirring a cauldron atop a peat fire that was set in the middle of the floor. That was strange enough, but what intrigued him even more was that, though the wind was now turning to a blast and the rain was thick and heavy, the smoke rose straight up, clumps of grass on the floor stood quite still and not a drop of water fell within. 'A witch!' he uttered under his breath. Unsure whether to be frightened or furious. He chose neither and, instead, walked fearlessly in. The woman looked up unperturbed, 'Fine night,' she said.

Jock was unsure whether it was a jest or that she really thought so, so he just said, 'Dae ye mind if a jyne ye?'

'Naw! Come ben an get a heat. Bit juist tak nae notice o whit a am aboot.'

'Cannae see a thing,' said the lad, wisely. 'A'll juist mak masel comfortable i the corner.

'Guid,' she said, continuing to stir.

Darkness settled in and with it came more witches. They barely gave Jock a look, preferring to stare into the cauldron. The first witch stopped stirring and they all joined hands and began circling the pot, chanting strange incantations. When they stopped another witch placed her hand in the pot, pulled out a blood-red bonnet and wrung the liquid out of it. She placed it on her head and recited, 'Hilloa for Cantyre!' Much to Jack's amazement, she shot straight up into the air and out of sight. A moment later the bonnet floated back down into the cauldron. Another witch carried out the same ritual and disappeared; the rest followed until all were gone. By now Jock was on his feet and walked over to the cauldron just as the hat once more floated down. Unable to resist the temptation Jack looked into the simmering blood-like liquid and saw the bonnet. He gingerly lifted it out and found it was quite cool. He wrung it out, placed it on his head and uttered the words, 'Hilloa for Cantyre'. In an instant he was airborne, soaring high over Cumbrae. He involuntarily screamed, half in fear and half in excitement. The speed was so great Jock was now hardly able to breathe, so he dragged the bonnet from his head and held it over his mouth and nose. He shot over Arran and the Sound of Kilbrannan and was gently deposited among a merry band of revellers on the Mull of Kintyre. It was a moment before he noticed that at its centre was Auld Hornie, Auld Clootie: the Deil himself. As he landed, he shoved the bonnet into his pocket. The Devil called for quiet and announced, to cheers, that tonight they would sup in the cellars of the King of France. The devil raised high his great wings, and all were swept up and away southwards. Jock delighted in the ride, whirling and swirling among warlocks and witches, trailing showers of light like a great comet. They shot earthwards, and in a blink were inside the great vaulted cellars of Versailles. Music appeared out of thin air and all began to drink and dance. In no time Jock was 'fou' and leaping about in a Highland Schottische with a comely sorceress. In his inebriated exultation he called out, 'Sae the Lord be thankit.' At the mention of the holy name the place was instantly dark and empty. Unable to find a

way out in the pitch-black, Jock dropped down against a wall and slid into a happy drunken slumber. A while later he was rudely awoken by two of the King's guard. His hands were tied behind his back and he was dragged before His Majesty. The king, who had a good grasp of English said, 'Explain yourself.'

Jock, who also had a good grasp of English and little grasp of sense, said, 'I didn't mean to insult Your Majesty, but I was with some witches and the Devil and…'

'What? Witches? The Devil?' roared the regent. 'You are to be taken out and hanged immediately.'

The horror-struck Jock was dragged to the front of the building, where a scaffold already stood, and pushed up on to a wide plank of wood. The hooded executioner walked from the opposite end and placed a rope about his neck. 'Do you have a last wish Englishman?' he said in a thick French accent.

'Scotchman.'

'You wish a Scotchman?'

'No! I am a Scotchman.'

'Oh! I like Scotchmen.'

'In that case, I wish you wouldn't hang me.'

The executioner looked up to the royal balcony where the king and queen stood, then back to Jock. 'So sorry my friend; not possible.'

'Well then, can I put on my bonnet?'

'Where is it?' said the hangman.

'In my right pocket.' said Jock nodding in that direction.

The Frenchman removed it and place it jauntily on Jock's head. 'Looks good. I must get one.'

'Come to Skelmorlie in Scotland anytime and I'll get one for you.' The man gave Jock a quizzical look before placing the rope round his neck. Jock looked at him and smiled, 'Hilloa for Largs,' he called and shot straight up in the air. Away over France, the Channel and England he flew, keeping his chin tucked into his chest. In a matter of minutes, he dropped down on to Largs beach. He exhaled heavily, then laughed a laugh of delight and relief. When he stopped laughing, he started again because round his neck was the rope and stuck to his shoes was the plank of wood. 'That'll dae fer ma boat.' He said. Suddenly he stopped, 'Curses,' he said, 'A suid hae said 'Skelmorlie'. Nou A hae tae walk the five miles hame.'

After untying himself Jock picked up the plank and ropes and set off home. It was a joyful walk, and on the way, he detoured by the derelict cottage. To his disappointment, it was empty. Once home he fixed his boat with the plank, replaced the rotten rope with the Hangman's noose and went out and caught a big cod.

Now that's the end of the tale … and the fish's.

30

In Shape o' Beast

It was nearing the end of the seventeenth century and superstition was rife. Witches and warlocks terrorised the countryside and the Devil was everywhere to be found, or so people thought. Now, to our tale:

Quentin Semple, a twelve-year-old Prestwick lad, was dragged before the magistrates having been found in the kailyard of a local baron helping himself to his peas. That the baron had usurped common land for his own purpose, or the age of the lad was not taken into regard, he was imprisoned to await trial. Young David Rankine, of a similar age and apprenticed to the town bailie, himself a lover of the baron's peas, knew where the key to the tolbooth was kept – under the bailie's pillow. With the nerve of youth and an innate nimbleness, David slipped into the bailie's bedroom and removed the key. With his keen nerve and good timing, he accessed the tolbooth and unlocked the cell door, freeing his compatriot. As they were leaving, the enterprising Rankine spied a young bull grazing nearby. Using a great clump of grass, he enticed the beast into the jail and locked him in the cell, before returning the key to its home under the bailie's pillow. Next day the magistrates and barons of the town were to sit in judgement of the young miscreant. By this time the stirk was impatient with his imprisonment and in a foul mood. As they paraded into the tolbooth they were greeted by a loud bellow from the creature. 'It's the Deil,' called the bailie and panic ensued. There was mayhem and bruised shoulders as the local great and good fought to leave.

Outside young David, his face a picture of innocence, enquired after the Semple boy.

'Guid God above,' said a magistrate, 'the Deil has consumit him.'

The aggrieved baron, now in fear of his immortal soul, cried out. 'We need tae get the meenister and lay the beast.'

'A'll gang an get him sirs,' said David, and off he ran.

At the manse David related the truth of what had transpired, in full knowledge that the minister spent his life in sufferance of the supercilious grandees of the town, with their airs and graces and un-Christian greed.

At the tolbooth the minister greeted the assembly and asked if any would like to join him to help with the exorcism. As none stepped forward, except David, he asked that they retire to their respective homes for an hour in case things got out of hand. The magistrates and barons were happy to oblige. He also asked the baillie to fetch the cell key, which he did, before retreating homeward.

After grabbing a handful of grass, the minister and young Rankine entered the tolbooth with apparent caution. Inside, the minister unlocked the door and placated the incarcerated stirk with the fodder. After a reasonable wait, he and David then led it out of doors and shooed it away towards the beach. When the hour was up, the local elite returned and were informed that the Deil was laid and that the young prisoner, in fact, had escaped his clutches. The dignitaries decided that because of his obvious trauma, there would be no further action taken against young Semple.

The minister took David aside and asked that he not do it again and to keep away from the baron's kailyard.

'It's no his kailyaird meenister. He thieved it frae the common fowk.'

'Perhaps so David, but maybe a sly word from the pulpit on Sunday will shame the rascal.'

'A doubt that, meenister. They folk dinnae ken the meanin o shame.'

David Rankine was not finished with his trickstering. At Halloween he and some friends went guising to the minister of St Quivox's manse and were given short shrift for their 'pagan practices'. At St Quivox church the rope for the bell hung on the outside of the tower. The young men led a cow to the building and tied its tail to the rope. The poor creature could only walk a short distance before it set off the bell. All night long as it grazed it caused the bell to ring in an erratic fashion. Local people, including the minister of the church, thought it was the Deil up to no good and stayed away. The following morning the reverend was left with egg on his face. As for David, he played his trick and the result was a treat.

'Trick or treat' is not an American creation. The name was first used in Alberta, Canada, then later adopted in the United States. Scottish 'guising'

is first recorded in Ontario in 1928, though undoubtedly existed there before. The idea of dressing up and travelling from door to door performing was known in Ancient Greece, however, the origins of dressing up (guising, galoshans or mumming) for Halloween – and other festivals – is recorded in Scotland in the sixteenth century and it was almost certainly this tradition that was exported to the New World.

In the South-West, guisers would travel from door to door and if they were refused, then the contents of the midden would be dumped on the doorstep or doors tied up and other such 'tricks'. Rev Walter Gregor recorded this 'trick or treating' in Galloway in 1895.

In the 1950s we went guising with costumes and masks (false faces) made by ourselves. Masks could be bought, but most of us made our own. At a door we would put on a silly voice and say, 'Can A hae ma Hallaeen?' We were expected to perform a song or a poem, but not before the people of the house guessed who we were. There was great pride in beating them.

31

John o Wuidheid's Wife

Where Glenapp falls away towards Loch Ryan there once stood the remnants of an ancient forest called the Woods of Finnart. These woodlands had the reputation of being the haunt of the sith, pronounced shee, or the fairy folk. The ancient denizens of the woodland realm had a mixed reputation. On the one hand they could be helpful and kindly, but just as often were prone to puckish tricks: the stealing of a child, giving bags of gold that turn into dead leaves, abducting unsuspecting musicians for a night that turn out to be seven years.

At the top of the forest was a farm, aptly named Wuidheid, and the man who worked its lands was named John, or more often, John o Wuidheid. One day John's wife discovered she was to have a baby, and after the usual term announced to her husband that she thought it might be best to send for the howdie or midwife. John quickly saddled his garron and a spare horse for the midwife and trotted off along the six-mile track to Cairn Ryan in Galloway. As he passed a place known as the Alders of Finnart he heard voices and halted briefly to hear the conversation. The main reason was that he had heard his own name mentioned. He soon realised that the voices were those of the sith and one strident voice proclaimed, 'Cut it short and thick like John o Wuidheid's wife.'

John realised that no good was afoot and urged on his horse towards the clachan. He was soon at the howdie's door and in less than five minutes, back on the road home. They travelled the track unmolested until nearly at Wuidheid when ahead of them came a procession of people lined up behind bearers carrying an open coffin. In it lay a body wrapped in a mort-claith or winding sheet. The howdie was alarmed, 'We suid gae back, it's ill tae meet a deid-kist on the wey tae a birthin.'

'Aye,' said John, 'But it will be mair unlucky no tae let it pass.' With this he urged both horses into the shadows of a thicket. Just as the procession passed, he rode out and threw his plaidie over the coffin. The mourners and coffin disappeared in an instant and John's wife dropped abruptly on to a soft clump of grass. She sat up as if waking from a dream.

He and the howdie dismounted to attend to her. Placing her on the spare horse, the midwife behind, all proceeded to Wuidheid where John settled his wife and the howdie in the byre while he went to the house. As he entered, he could hear howls of pain, as of a woman giving birth and a counterfeit howdie calling, 'Push Woman! Push!' The noise was loud enough to make his ears ring. The kitchen and ben were full of women, all clucking and chattering. 'Let me in', said John, 'A'll see if a guid scowther will hurry things alang.' A louder howl followed.

'Oh sir, dae ye hear that?' wailed one of the women, 'She canne pit aff a meenit langer.'

John threw a load of peats on the fire and gave them a blast with the bellows. In no time flames were licking up towards the rigging, threatening to set the thatch alight. He piled on more until the heat would have roasted a pig. 'Nou,' said Wuidheid, 'If we fling her on the low, that'll quate her.' The women looked on in disbelief and horror as John advanced on the bed. There was a piercing scream, then silence. When John pulled back the cover, the writhing stopped and all that remained was an alder log, short and stumpy, like his wife. When the farmer turned around, the assembly of woman had disappeared. John o Wuidheid went out to the byre and brought in his guidwife and the howdie, who, shorly after, delivered a healthy, plump baby boy.

32

Johnny Faa

There are many different versions of this tale, none of which seems historically accurate. The facts seem to suggest that no such event ever occurred, or if it did, it involved other people. This story is set in the early sixteenth century, the most usual time, and conveys a scenario that fits with some of the history and known facts about Sir Gilbert and Lady Jane Kennedy.

THE COUNTESS AND THE GYPSY

There is another River Tyne that flows out of the Moorfoot Hills in the Lothians and enters the Firth of Forth at Belhaven. On its way it passes Tyninghame House seat of the Earl of Haddington. The earl had a beloved daughter, Jane, who, with her own private retinue, were wont to walk to the riverbank where they would play the lute, sing and dance. It was on such a day in late May when trees were in blossom and young birds were leaving their nests to fly out into the wide world that Lady Jane and her cohort of young women went out to play. As the girls laughed and danced, a group of young men approached but kept their distance, except for one young blade, who danced towards them and wove his way through the group. While his companions were plainly and even rudely dressed, the young buck was attired in fine clothes: an embroidered velvet doublet and breeches, well cut boots and a blue silk bonnet with a white cockade, which he duly took off and made an exaggerated bow to the company. The girls looked on in shock at this apparent effrontery. When Jane laughed and applauded, her retinue nervously followed her example.

'Forgive my intrusion, sweet ladies, but I was enamoured, enthralled, even glamourised at such an agreeable company and the gaiety with which you conduct yourselves.' As he spoke his dark eyes settled on Lady Jane and seemed to look deep into her soul. A tingle of excitement ran through her and she felt light-headed and giddy. He looked away at the other girls and began to dance among them but always coming back to Lady Jane. He offered his hand and as she took it, the effect was electrifying, and thrills coursed the length of her body causing her to stumble. In an instant she was caught and held. The feel of his strong arms about her only served to heighten the sensuousness. The young man helped her to a large boulder and bade her sit. She recovered and took a deep breath, 'I am so sorry,' she said, 'I don't know what came over me.'

'The day is getting hot, milady,' he said, 'You have, perhaps, over-exerted yourself.'

'Yes, of course. It must be that.' By now her companions had crowded round and the young blade respectfully moved away.

Lady Jane recovered her composure, 'I think I shall return home,' she said.

As she lay abed in the late evening Jane could not sleep for thinking of this young man who had touched a place deep within her she never knew existed. There were always young men around the castle, but she would never have thought any more of them being her beau than she would her brother. This young man carried an aura of glamourie, enchantment and danger. Had he said he was a sorcerer, she would have fully believed in him. It was a week later at the mercat in Haddington that she encountered him again. A crowd had gathered around some performance and were calling, cheering and laughing. Out of curiosity she eased her way through the throng - there was little problem, for the spectators gave way before this lady of rank. She could see. above the heads of the crowd, small leather balls rising and falling. 'Just a juggler,' she thought and was about turn away when she saw that it was the young man from a fortnight before. Slowly she pushed to the front. The youth was engaged in hurling seven balls into the air. Every few moments he would spin around, kicking up dust with his boot, but not missing a beat. He would alter the rhythm, throw his arms wide, throw from behind his back; it was mesmerising. As he moved around, he was suddenly facing her, their eyes met and the balls tumbled from the sky hitting his head and shoulders, causing general amusement. One rolled and stopped at the foot of Lady Jane. He smiled, his face lighting up like summer, again bedazzling her. He took two steps forward and gave an exaggerated bow, at the same time deftly lifting the runaway ball. He balanced it on the tip of his right index finger and offered it to her. 'Milady?' She looked him full in the eyes then plucked it. The crowd applauded. He turned about and graciously accepted the praise and thrown coins, palms to the sky. He then picked up his coat and slipped it on, gathered up the leather bag it lay on, the balls and the coins. These he put in the bag and turned back to Jane as the crowd dissipated. 'You are still here.'

'Yes,' she said, 'I hoped you would do more.'

'Then I will.' He removed three balls from the pouch and proceeded to juggle them with one hand then two. He caught the balls and offered them to her.

She dropped her head bashfully, 'I would just drop them.'

'That's how you learn,' he said. 'Perhaps I can teach you. Tomorrow, mid-afternoon, come to the river where we met. Now, I must go.' He stepped back, took a deep bow and was gone.'

She had wanted him to stay longer, to talk, to know his name. She would be at the river tomorrow.

Not wishing to seem too eager she arrived a little later with a trusted handmaiden as an escort, but there was no sign of the young man. She tried to hide her disappointment and sat on the riverbank in the warm afternoon sun watching the water and wishing. 'So glad you came,' said a voice from behind. Her head spun round, as did the handmaiden's, and there he was with a companion.

'Oh! You gave me a fright; I didn't hear you come,' she said, her hand on her chest.

'I apologise Milady, but it is the way of the Roma.'

'The Romans?' she said.

'No, Roma; what you call the Gypsies. They call me their king,' he said dropping down beside her. Much to the discomfort of Jane's chaperone. The fact that Gypsy's companion sat behind her did in no way ease the discomfort.

'You are King of the Gypsies?' said Lady Jane.

'Yes, Johnny Faa, King of the Roma, at your service.'

'You don't look like a Gy...Roma'

'I don't look like a king either, but what does a Roma look like?'

She hesitated, as if looking for the right word, then flushed red, 'Like a Gypsy,' then laughed in embarrassment.

'I have brown eyes, black hair my skin is darker to show that I am from far away.'

'My father has men with brown eyes, black hair and dark skin from working in the fields.'

'Oh! you noticed, did you? Ah! Now I understand,' he said gently mocking.

'I didn't mean it like that, I just noticed when passing.'

Johnny nodded his face full of mock scepticism. She punched him on the upper arm, noticing the powerful muscles beneath.

'You say you are King of the Roma.'

'People say that I am, but truth to tell, I am Lord and Earl of Little Egypt by royal appointment of good King James himself. There is only room for one king in a country.'

It was Jane's chance to nod with mock scepticism.

'Truly,' he said, opening his leather satchel and withdrawing a velum parchment. He handed it to her.

'Gracious!' she exclaimed, 'The Privy Seal.'

'Indeed, did I not say?' He gave her a serious look, 'I am a man of honour, Milady.'

She read the parchment which began, 'oure louit Johnne Faw, lord and erle of Litill Egipt' (our beloved Johnne Faw, Lord and Earl of Little Egypt) 'Where is Little Egypt?' she asked.

'In the west, milady; in the homeland of the mighty Robert the Bruce. It is called Carrick. It is now in the possession of the Kennedy clan; a more ruthless, self-serving band of brigands you will not meet. They guard their lands with an iron fist and have little time for us Roma. Therefore, I am here in the Lothians.'

She looked hard at the man before her, his deep, dark eyes, his sunned skin, the dash of his clothes and the way he sat, proud without being haughty. She looked away but longed to look at him endlessly. She rolled up the parchment and handed it to him. For an instant their hands touched. She tremored as her nervous system jangled. The effect on him seemed similar. He lifted his hand and kissed the place where contact had been made. That simple gesture made her fall in love with him.

They met many times over the summer, mainly along the river, and even her chaperone seemed less reserved and talked and laughed with Johnny's companion. As August began and the Lamasstide was celebrated, news came that King James was asking for knights to go to France to aid their allies. The Auld Alliance, first created in 1295, was still active and when France called to help ward off the English, Scotland honoured the ancient accord. It was with a heavy heart that he bid farewell to his love. She abandoned formality and wrapped her arms about him, 'Promise me you will return.'

'I will live for you, stay alive for you and will return to you, though I know not when.'

Lady Jane untied a royal-blue, silk ribbon from her hair and tied it about his right upper arm, 'Bring this back to me.'

'I will Milady.'

John Faa went off to war and Lady Jean went back to her castle to thole their long parting. But in those long-ago times a young woman's view of the world and her dreams were not the consideration of those who held power over them. Her father was the Earl of Haddington and he had other ideas. Politics was the lifeblood of the aristocracy and vying for power was always the game. Power could be bought, it could be taken, and it could be obtained by arrangement. This was done through alliances, and the easiest form of alliance was through marriage. So, arrangements were made for Lady Jane to marry Sir Gilbert Kennedy, Earl of Cassillis. Jane's father began the arrangements but had not reckoned on the tenacity and stubbornness of his daughter, 'I will not marry that man. I do not know him and do not wish to know him; besides, are they not all savages, these men of the West?

'Savage they may be, but they often hold the balance of power, and that works well for us.'

'Yes, for you; but not for me. You married mother for love, did you not?'

'Yes, but that is not the rule. I had known your mother since we were children.'

'Nonetheless, I will marry for love. I will marry Sir John Faa, Lord and Earl of Little Egypt.'

The earl's eyes opened in astonishment, 'The Egyptian?'

'No! He is king of the Egyptians and beloved of King James,' she looked away, 'and of me.'

Lady Jane refused to budge; but as Johnny had not returned after a year and there were rumours of his death, she began to weaken. At last she agreed that if he had not returned after another year and a day, she would agree to her father's request. A month later an official letter arrived with the stamp of Scottish Ambassador in Paris confirming the death of Sir John Faa who died gallantly protecting the sovereign state of France from the depredations of the perfidious English.

Lady Jean crumpled in a heap, letting out a wail of despair. Her father comforted her, pained at the hurt of his child, but happy that his little ruse had succeeded, and John Faa had been detained in France. A month later

Lady Jane became the Countess of Cassillis.

Sir Gilbert Kennedy was typical of his family: pious and ruthless. Whatever he did, he knew he had the backing of Heaven. He preached love, but a hard love: spare the rod and spoil the child. The dark Presbyterianism of Scotland. He was undoubtedly fond of his wife but showed no warmth. Even in intimacy, it was an act of duty and not passion. As for Lady Jane, she found him distant, cold, preoccupied with matters of the church and the running of his estates. Her time was often spent in solitude or wandering the banks and braes along the River Doon. She would sit and contemplate the slow moving current as it eased its way to the firth. In summer, to her delight, she watched the swallows skim the surface, gathering up insects or drinking on the wing, a long chevron left in their wake. One such day, while her husband was busy organising a journey on matters of the kirk, she sat on the riverside composing simple rhymes in her head. Then something invaded her musings, a presence. She turned in fright. The shock doubled as she saw, standing before her, the noble face of Johnny Faa, a royal-blue silk ribbon in his hand. Almost fainting with emotion, she tried to stand, but stumbled. He caught her, drew her up and embraced her passionately. She held him, never wanting to let him go, 'My John, my John,' she said, through tears of joy. 'They said you were dead.'

'I know, I know. I was detained by our own people and I guessed the reason. Your father is a powerful man and he used that power to keep us apart. But he will not succeed. We will leave together and go over the border into England where they cannot touch us, and then on to Wales. I have family there.'

She held him more tightly, 'My husband is at home but intends to go to Edinburgh on kirk business. When he leaves, I can gather up a valise for the journey.'

'When does he leave?'

'I'm not sure, but I think it is tomorrow.'

'I will return the day after tomorrow before dawn. Where will I meet you?'

'Along the river towards the castle there is a ford with a set of stepping-stones. I will be there before the cock crows'

The Countess did her best to hide her growing excitement. The worst part was the waiting. The hours oozed by before her husband departed with a troop of retainers, thirty strong - in these dangerous times it was wise for a wealthy nobleman to have adequate protection. In secret Lady Jane prepared a bag for the elopement. It had to be light enough for her to carry, so she dispensed with clothes except a few items of underwear and filled it instead with valuables. There was no sleep for her that night. She watched the candles burn marking the hours, then at four o' clock she made her way barefoot from her room to the great front door. Silently, she slid the great bar and opened the door wide enough for her to slip through. There was some summer light for her to find her way to the ford. When she arrived, she saw the silhouette of her beloved John across the water. She nimbly crossed and embraced him. He leaned in and said quietly, 'I have with me a dozen men who will take us to the border. They are camped a few hundred yards away, for fear of the horses alerting the castle. Let us go, and quickly.'

As the lovers made their escape Sir Gilbert rode in a fury, not to Edinburgh, but back to the castle: his secretary had left an important document behind. If they rode hard, they would still reach Edinburgh in time. He arrived at the castle at five-o'-clock and found the castle servants in a state of excitement. The front door was found to be open and Lady Jane was missing. The Earl sent men and women in all directions to find any sign of his missing wife. It was not long before one of his troop found the hoofprints of at least a dozen horses and the chase was on.

Meanwhile Johnny Faa, Lady Jane and their dozen protectors rode steadily up the Doon towards Dalmellington. Their intended route would take them by Dumfries and round the Solway to the protection of Carlisle. From there they would then ride south and into North Wales and join the Romanichal who were escaping the persecution of the English crown. They entered Glen Muck, the glen of the pig, a mile south of Dalmellington, and as they began the climb out of the glen they found the way barred by a troop of armed riders. John Faa was an experienced and skilled soldier, as were his men, but attacking uphill, and with Lady Jane, it would be suicidal. They had to retreat. They turned about only to find their way blocked. Escape up the sides of the glen would be impossible. Their fate was inevitable.

At the head of the northern pursuers rode Sir Gilbert. As he approached, Johnny leaped from the saddle and ingloriously dragged Lady Jane from her saddle, drew a dirk and held it to her throat, 'Say nothing my love,' he whispered in her ear, then he shouted to the Kennedy, 'Come any closer and your wife dies. The earl drew his horse to a halt. 'You can have her back safely on condition my twelve men go free.'

'No John,' she said in despair, 'We will die together.'

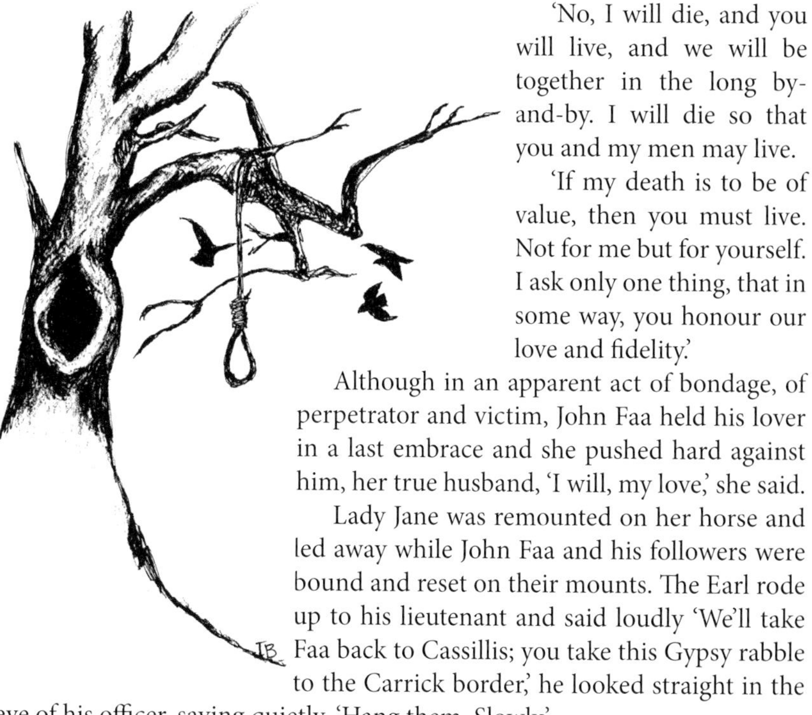

'No, I will die, and you will live, and we will be together in the long by-and-by. I will die so that you and my men may live.

'If my death is to be of value, then you must live. Not for me but for yourself. I ask only one thing, that in some way, you honour our love and fidelity.'

Although in an apparent act of bondage, of perpetrator and victim, John Faa held his lover in a last embrace and she pushed hard against him, her true husband, 'I will, my love,' she said.

Lady Jane was remounted on her horse and led away while John Faa and his followers were bound and reset on their mounts. The Earl rode up to his lieutenant and said loudly 'We'll take Faa back to Cassillis; you take this Gypsy rabble to the Carrick border,' he looked straight in the eye of his officer, saying quietly, 'Hang them. Slowly.'

Johnny Faa, was taken to Cassillis, and in sight of the countess's bedroom window, was hanged from the Dule Tree until dead. The King of the Gypsies went out of this life and into legend.

Lady Jane returned to her life as countess and wife of the earl, but she often longed to be away from the Cassillis and its memories, and so spent her time in solitude in the castle at Maybole. In time she learned the fate of Johnny's men, so she asked that around her window be carved thirteen heads. Each day while there, at the hour her lover was hung, she prayed before the window. Those who saw the carvings saw Jesus and his followers, Lady Jane saw Johnny Faa and his.

A dule tree or dool tree was where criminals were publicly hanged. The word means grief or suffering. Probably the same word as the archaic English word dole (as in doleful). Origin from Latin dolor (as in dolorous).

The following poem and story are from a worldwide folktale and song. The writer has heard it told in Greece, though that concerned a pirate rather than the Devil. It is thoroughly misogynistic, or perhaps it shows that a woman can best even the Devil. The song version is by Robert Burns. The first verse is complete with the song's repetitive refrain, but the piece minus the refrain is below to show the story in an easier form. A prose version is below that. Kellyburn Braes lies between Skelmorlie and Wemyss Bay. The Kelly Burn forms the border between Ayrshire and Renfrewshire.

Kellyburn Braes
(Robert Burns)

There lived a carle on Kellyburn Braes *man*
Hey and the rue grows bonny with thyme
An he had a wife wis the plague o his days
And the thyme it is withered, and rue is in prime

Ae day as the carl gaed up the lang glen, *one, went, long valley*
He met wi the Deil, says 'Hoo dae ye fen?' *fend/exist (How are you?)*

'I've got a bad wife, sir, that's aa ma complaint,
Fer, savin yer presence, to her ye're a saint.'

'It's neither your stot nor your staig I shall crave, *bullock, young horse*
But gie me your wife, man, for her I must have.'

'O welcome, maist kindly,' the blythe carl said, *cheerful*
'But if ye can match her ye're waur than ye're caad.' *worse, called*

The de'il has got the auld wife on his back, And like a puir pedlar he's carried his pack.	
Now he's ta'en her hame to his ain hallan door. Syne bade her gae in fer a bitch and a hure.	*home, inside porch* *then, go, bad tempered and mean*
Then straucht he maks fifty, the pick o his band, Turn oot on her guard in the clap o a hand,	*straight*
The carlin gaed thro' them like ony wud bear, Whaeer she got hands on cam near her nae mair.	*woman, went, wood* *whoever*
A reekit wee deevil looks ower the waa 'O help, maister, help, or she'll ruin us aa! '	*smoky*
The Devil he swore by the edge o his knife, He pitied the man that wis tyed tae a wife.	
The Devil he swore by the kirk an the bell He was no in wedlock, thank Heaven, but in Hell	*church*
Then Satan he travelled again wi his pack, An tae her auld husband he's cairrit her back.	*carried*
'I hae been a Devil the feck o my life But neer was in hell till I met wi' a wife.'	*large amount/most* *never*

There was a man who lived on Kellyburn Braes, a place famous for its plants and wildflowers, such a thyme and rue. In the time of our story, the thyme had withered and rue was in its prime. One day, after his daily upset with his wife, he had taken a walk to cool off. As the man walked along the long glen, whom should he meet but the Devil. 'Hou are ye? asked the Devil, as though he cared.

'Dinnae ask,' said the man. 'That wife o mine; she wuid challenge the patience o a saint. In fact, beside her you seem a saint.'

The Devil said, 'Sounds like my kind of woman.' Then raising an eyebrow, he said to the man, 'I'd be glad to take her off yer hands.'.

'Gin ye can haunle her, sir, ye can hae her.'

In a flash the devil was in the man's house, threw his wife on his back and was off home to Hell.

When he reached the front door of Hell, he pulled her off his back and threw her in.

She had no sooner landed on her feet than she saw ten young devils hanging on a wire, so she promptly kicked them in the fire.

She saw another three hanging on chains and so kicked out their brains.

One wee devil sitting on a wall called to the Devil, 'Come and save us before she kills us all.'

So, the Devil put her on his back and delivered her to her husband, saying, 'I may be the Devil, but I never was in Hell until I met your wife.'

The additional pieces in the prose section are taken from other variations of the song.

34

King's Shilling

This story I love. It is about comeuppance for meanness which is, I think, the greatest sin. We survive in part because of ourselves and in part because of our family; but one and all are part of a group, whether it be a native of Largs, Ayr, Girvan, all of Ayrshire or even Scotland and beyond, and our survival finally depends on the way we aid or work with each other. It is also said that the measure of a society or an individual is how it treats those who are most vulnerable. On with the story:

A farmer from Kyle had a good harvest, unlike the other farmers about who had experienced a bad season. Because of the shortage there was a rush to buy and soon all the farms were sold out. All, that is, except our seemingly fortunate farmer. He held on to his store then raised the prices to maximise his profits. This meant that many who had small incomes could only afford less meal and winter was coming on. A poor widow with a string of children to feed joined the queue to buy her winter store. She was one shilling short of the required amount and asked that the farmer show a little charity by allowing her a few weeks to pay the balance. The farmer was unmoved, 'Charity begins at hame. Nae money, nae meal.'

'Please sir. Ye ken me, ye can trust me tae pey.'

'A trust naebody,' he said coldly, 'Neist!'

The now distraught woman turned to leave when a passing soldier cut in, 'Haud on ma jo, whit ails ye?'

'A am but a shillin short o purchasin ma winter store o meal, an the fermer will nae gie me grace o a few weeks tae pey the balance.'

The soldier turned to the farmer, 'Fegs man. A wee bit o God's grace fer a body less fortunat than yersel. She means tae pey ye and a hae nae doot she will.'

'Weel a dae.'

'Wuid ye accept ma shillin?'

'If ye are fond eneuch tae pey, then aye.'

The soldier turned to the waiting buyers, held up the shilling and tossed it to the farmer who grabbed it out of the air and put it in his pouch. The soldier gave a laugh, 'Ye are aa witness tae the fact that oor guid fermer here has acceptit the shillin.' He then lifted the bag of meal and presented it to the widow, 'There ye gang ma dearie, A hope ye and yer bairnies hae a guid winter.' He gave an exaggerated salute and marched off up the road to Kilmarnock.

Two days later, as the farmer sat supping a cog of brose, there came a heavy knock on his door. When he opened it, he was confronted by the soldier and two burly companions, 'Get yer coat, ye are comin wae us.'

The protesting farmer was seized and frogmarched to the military barracks in Kilmarnock where he was duly informed that having accepted the King's Shilling, and in front of witnesses, he was now a member of King George's forces. It would a long time before his next harvest.

35

The name Loveable Rogue has been applied to many characters, real and otherwise. From Robert Burns to Long John Silver they have made their mark on our minds. One lesser known, but famous in his time, was the Laird of Changue.

Changue is largely in Carrick on the north side of the Galloway mountains and lies between the rivers Minnoch and the Stinchar. In the time of our telling the land was impoverished, the people living in hovels and starvation was the lot of everyone. Even the Laird of Changue, an already notorious, devil-may-care smuggler was down to his last few bawbees. His cows were dry, his oats dead in the field and his orchards with barely any fruit. 'Ach weel,' he said to himself fatalistically, 'There's aye the Kirkdamdie Fair.'

The annual fair held at Barr saw traders, farmers, cotters, along with a kenspeckle band of jugglers, wrestlers, fiddlers, pipers, storytelling travellers and gypsies. There would be slim pickings for anyone; but they still came, if only for the drams of illicit spirit that was distilled in the hills about the clachan.

Trading was poor, as expected, so all the more reason for passing about a quaich of usquebeatha. Acquaintances from further away, with siller in their pouches, stood the ebullient Changue a few rounds; as much to goad him into swordfighting and wrestling, as was his wont. But he needed little encouragement, and though few could take on the professional wrestlers, Changue was one of those who could not only take them on, but beat them at their own game - sober or drunk. So, while pipers piped, fiddlers fiddled, and lusty dancers threw themselves into another 'Strip the Willow', Changue took on the best and came out best.

Drinking and storytelling went on well into the wee hours, with the laird among the loudest and bawdiest of them all. The night drew on and, as bodies threw their plaidies about them and slipped into slumber, Changue took the rough road home. While still going in generally the right direction, he had, however, lost the track and found himself stumbling through bracken and heather and tripping over the boulders of his tumbled wilderness. After one trip too many, he settled himself under an overhanging rock and fell asleep. But it was the sleep of a troubled man, and instead of resolution, his troubles seemed to pile higher until he was being swept away in an avalanche of debt and despair. He sat up suddenly, suffocating under his blanket of boulders, only to bash his head on the overhang. As he fell back, a soothing voice played in his head, 'Why worry? You always took the easy road to wealth and fortune, why not do so again?'

'Whit road? Wha are ye?'

'I'm your saviour, if you wish.'

'Lord Jesus,' exclaimed Changue.

'Not exactly,' said the voice, 'I'm from a bit lower down the ladder, you might say. Anyway, for a small price I can ease your worries and, perhaps, make your fortune.'

'Nou ye hae ma attention. Whit is the smaa price?'

'Well, you still have half your life to live and, in that time, you can have great wealth, joy and pleasure. At the end of that time, the pleasure will be mine, for I will claim your immortal soul.'

'You want ma immortal saul?' said the laird, quizzically.

'Not now. What I want now is the promise of your soul.'

Changue thought for a moment: perhaps it was the bang on the head that caused this hallucination. Even if it were Auld Hornie, the end of his life was a long way off. 'Agreed,' he said, recklessly, not quite sure what he was agreeing to. As he lay there musing over what had just transpired, he fell back asleep.

The cool dew-laden morning brought him to consciousness. As he unsteadily hauled himself to his feet, he thought more on the dream, if it was such. Maybe it was a whisper of what was to come, but he shrugged it aside.

Quite suddenly things improved for the laird: his hens began to lay, the kailyard produced a generous harvest, as did his oats and barley. The orchard was in thick blossom in the spring and by the end of August apples, pears and plums hung thick from the branches. Even his smuggling improved, and he was always two steps ahead of the exciseman. Moreover, his good

fortune continued into old age. So it was a great surprise to everyone when the seemingly ageless laird was stricken by a fever. He turned a sickly yellow, his hair hung lank about his head and his muscular frame gradually wasted away. Doctors could find no explanation or cure and his family prepared for his passing. One day, tired of the incessant intrusions, he requested that he be left in peace for a while. As he lay there, eyes closed, preparing to meet his maker, he felt a presence in the room. On opening his eyes, he was confronted with a handsome man dressed all in black. Assuming he was a doctor or priest, the laird asked him politely to go, 'I shall go, sir; but only to wait for you in your garden and thence to take you with me to eternal damnation.'

'Whit!' exclaimed the laird loudly, rising on to his left elbow.

'We have a long-standing agreement,' said the man, 'I gave you a life of ease and luxury and all that I asked was your immortal soul, on which you agreed.' The dark stranger took a step back, 'I will see you shortly.'

Changue fell back and threw his right arm over his eyes in disbelief. Was this another dream, or was the hallucination he had on the night of Kirkdamdie Fair a reality? He had lived a charmed life, everyone said so; 'Ye hae the luck o the Deil,' they said. Perhaps he did indeed have the luck of the Devil and now he was about to pay with an eternity of torment.

With a growl he hauled himself off the bed and pulled on his boots, 'No gif ma name be the Laird o Changue.' Digging deep into his natural power he crossed the room, grabbed his sword from the wall and strode out of the door. As he passed through the willow arch into the garden he saw before him the great beast in all his satanic majesty: a monstrous scaly body with claws where there should have been hands and feet, a huge head that resembled some prehistoric lizard, atop which was set a pair of massive horns. Curling about him, as if it was some separate serpent, was his tail. But no snake had such a deadly sting. Rising behind him was a pair of vast leathery wings. The laird advanced on Satan and confronted him boldly, 'Gif ye want ma saul, ye maun tak it frae me.' Thus said, he jammed the tip of the blade into the grass before him and scored a large circle. 'This oath a mak: if ye can pit me oot o this circle. then ye maun tak me; gif no, ma debt is cancellit.'

The Devil attempted to enter the circle, but a stab to the foot made him swiftly withdraw. In a fury he swung his poisonous tail at the laird who ducked and at the same time swung the sword in an arc slicing off the fatal sting. Satan clawed at the laird and lost two fingers in the process, and his attempt to gore his adversary ended with the loss of a horn. Now howling with rage and fury the, the Prince of Darkness spread his immense wings and rose up in an attempt to fall on and crush the man. With all the skill of a someone who has blithely tripped out of the way of danger all his life, the Laird of Changue nimbly side-stepped the beast and at the same time sheared the wings off at the root. The Evil One crashed on to and through the earth back into the pit where-from he came.

The laird's family hearing the commotion came running into the garden a moment after the Devil's defeat. They found the victor kneeling by his sword, which he now held to form the sign of the cross, and thanked God for his deliverance and asked forgiveness for his foolishness. As he stood up, the family were overjoyed to see his recovery and he continued to live an honest life for many years. But, in time, even a man who has outwitted the Devil cannot outwit his own mortality, and so the Laird of Changue passed into history and legend.

Kirkdamdie (Kirk Dominae) at times known as Kildinine, Kildamonie and Kundamonie is at the Barr on the River Stinchar. The fair, from time immemorial, was held on the last Saturday in May.

36

In Middle English and Old Scots there was a letter known as yoch (Old English yogh) ȝ and made a y sound. To represent this, medieval printers, who largely came from Europe and did not have the letter in their cases (upper for capitals and lower for small print), substituted a z, which is why names and places in Scotland have the unsounded z. The classic place name is, of course, Culzean Castle in Carrick. For a full list see Yogh in Wikipedia.

Originally Culzean was a fortified tower, which was integrated into the present castle, and had stood there since at least the 1500s. Then it was known as Coif or Cove Castle - Co for short - in reference to the caves that puncture the cliffs below. The masters of Carrick were the Kennedys and Co was their show of power.

From its earliest times Co was famous for its gardens and the Laird of Co was not afraid to get his hands dirty, ensuring that they were just so. It was one day, while in the gardens clearing up at the back-end of the year, that a boy appeared quite suddenly beside him. As tough and hardened a man as Kennedy was, it still gave him quite a start, for there had been no one nearby just a moment before. 'Sairy for stertlin ye great sir, but ma mither is nane too weel and she bid me ask if yer lairdship wuid be sae kind as tae fill her stowp wi a wee drappie wine.' The boy held up a wooden tankard.

The laird smiled at the diminutive boy, 'Aye laddie I'm shuir we can spare a wee drappie fer yer mither.' He turned to and shouted over one of the gardeners, 'Adam, can ye tak this laddie tae the cellar an fill the stowp fer him.'

The young gardener tugged at his bonnet, 'Aye sir.' He then led the youth into the towerhouse

As they left the laird called out, 'I hope yer mither gets weel suin lad. Gie her ma blessins.'

'A wull sir; an blessins on yersel.'

At the towerhouse the gardener lit a brand and led him down to the cellar where he placed the torch in a holder on the wall. The floor was flagged in stone and contained baskets and boxes of stored vegetables, fruit, nuts; there were flagons of cordials and ten large barrels of wine. The young man pointed to a spigot on the nearest barrel, 'There ye gang. Help yersel laddie.'

'Thank ye sir,' said the lad and turned the handle. Blood red wine poured out into the tankard and after what seemed enough time to fill it, it continued to draw the liquid; on and on the wine flowed and still the tankard wasn't filled. The gardener 'Whit's gaun on?'

The boy turned to him and smiled, 'The laird said tae fill it, an that's juist whit a'm daein.' He turned back to his task.

The gardener watched in horror as he emptied the barrel, then moved to the next and started work on it. The young man fled up the stairs and into the garden. He found the laird, 'Sir, sir! That wee fella has emptied a hale barrel intae his stowp an has stertit on another.

The laird ran his hand through his hair, 'That's guy queer.' He gave shrug., 'Weell, A said he cuid fill the stowp, sae we maun lea him be. Awa an see hou he's gettin on.'

The young man ran back to the cellar just in time to see the tankard fill. The boy straightened up, 'That's me,' he said

The gardener lifted down the torch and started up the stairs. He got to the top and turned about: the boy was not there. He went back down the stairs, but the lad had disappeared. Later, the laird asked the young to breathe on him to check he hadn't helped himself while he was at it. He accepted the veracity of his story when he checked his barrels.

In the sixteenth century, Scotland still maintained an alliance with France, and Kennedy had gone with other Scottish mercenaries to assist them in the Italian Wars. Alas the French were defeated by an alliance of the Papal states, Spain, the Holy Roman Empire and the Auld Enemy – England. At the Battle of Mirabello the laird was captured, and being so far from Scotland with little hope of a ransom being paid he was doomed for execution. His prison was, ironically, a fortified tower not unlike Co. In the evening before his decapitation he wrote a letter to his wife hoping that, however unlikely, it would find its way to her. He had just folded the parchment and was dripping red wax to seal it when the diminutive boy appeared beside him. As before, the laird started back in shock, 'Fegs lad, a've haed cannons and arquebuses firit et me, A've haed swords slashed at me, daggers thrust at me and the only time A get a fricht is fae a shilpit, wee craitur. Whit brings ye this airt?

'A've cam tae tak ye hame,' said the boy, matter-of-factly.

'Bluid o the Aamichtie, hoo are ye proposin tae dae that.'

'On ma shouthers.'

Kennedy sat back in the chair and crossed his arms, 'On yer shouthers?' His voice rose an octave.

'Aye,' he said, opening the door on to the parapet of the keep. The laird followed the boy out into the night air. The lad hunkered down, 'Climb on sir.'

The whole scene was so surreal that the laird, as much out of curiosity, did as he was bid. The boy looked up, 'Haud on ticht tae ma juip.' The laird gripped the tunic and before he could utter another word, the lad said,

'Laird o Co,
Rise an go!'

… and leaped from the parapet. Kennedy's howl was quite involuntary. At the moment of impact, the lad once more took off into the air and, with great bounds that took in vast distances at a time, he covered the lands of Lombardy, France, England and Galloway. With one last great leap they landed in the gardens of Co Castle. In the bright light of an early spring moon the laird stood up and looked down at the smiling face of the boy, 'Whit can a say laddie? Ye hae saufit the hide o this worthless sinner and A will aye be grateful.'

The boy shook his head,

'Naw! Fer the kindness ye shawed tae ma mither,
Ae guid turn deserves anither.'

In an instant he disappeared.

37

Laird o Auchenskeith

The Laird of Auchenskeith was sitting quietly in his abode bothering no one and not wanting to be bothered when there came a great pounding at his door. He grudgingly rose out of his chair and peeked out the window but could see nothing. He went to the door and looked out and still there was nothing then a voice with an Irish accent from above said, 'Are ye Auchenskeith?' The laird looked up into the face of a very big man: a giant, in fact.

'I am.'

'Then ye are an eegit.'

'I'm sure you are right. Goodbye.' Auchenskeith closed the door and returned to his chair.

There came another knock, which he ignored, then the knocking grew more incessant. Auchenskeith went to the door. 'What do you want?'

'I want to mock you for the eegit ye are.'

'And why would you want to do that?'

'Because you are an eegit and so was the mother that spawned ye.'

Now Auchenskeith always took insults on the chin. They never bothered him at all, but to insult his mother was another matter, 'Wait there a minute,' he said. A moment later he came back with a very large sword. 'If you don't go back to where you came from, I will take yer head off your shoulders.'

'Can't you take a joke?' said the giant.

'Jokes I can take, but not about my mother. Remove yourself or your head will be removed.'

'It's only words,' protested the Irish Ettin

'And this is only a sword.' With that he took a swing at the giant's leg. Big as he was, he nimbly leaped out of the way.

'Yer mother was an eegit', he called one last time and ran off. The laird took after him and chased him past Dalry, all the way down past Kilwinning and through the Eglinton Woods where the giant tore out a beech tree and made to crush Auchenskeith with it. Using his warlock powers the laird leaped high in the air and lopped off the giant's hand at the wrist. Hand and tree crashed to the ground and the giant made off home across the Irish Sea. Auchenskeith went back to his chair. It is said that the tree and the attached hand could be seen for centuries from as far away as a mile.

THE LAIRD OF AUCHENSKEITH AND THE WITCH OF AUCHENMADE

The Laird of Auchenskeith near Dalry was sitting at his desk doing estate paperwork when a commotion outside his house followed by banging on his door drew him away. At the door was one of his farmhands, 'Sir, there's coos in the barley an a cannae get them oot fer the mad bull thet's amang them.' Together they ran to the field. Passing an old stone barn, the laird ran in and grabbed a pitchfork. At the field the cows, led by the bull, were rampaging up and down, flattening the crop. Fearlessly the laird ran at the bull which turned and faced him snorting with unrestrained violence. It dropped its head and charged. The laird, a highly trained warrior from the continental wars, waited until the last moment then nimbly leaped aside out of the way of the lethal horns. At the same time, he lunged with the pitchfork but missed his mark. The bull turned in an instant, clods of earth and barley stalks flying. It stopped, pawed the earth then charged again, tail high. The farmworker watched in alarm as the one-and-a-half-ton beast bore down on his master. What alarmed him most was that the laird held the pitchfork straight ahead of him. The force of collision would tear his arms off. A mere six feet from the thundering titan the laird threw himself in the air, turned full-circle and landed to the side of the bull. At the same time the pitchfork was driven into the front leg just above the left hoof. The animal tripped and virtually somersaulted, landing in a massive cloud of dust. Using the fork as a goad he herded the limping animal into the barn, the cows followed. Inside the animals roared in agitation then fell silent, so the laird entered, followed by the cautious worker. The cows were there, but there was no sign of the bull. As the laird pushed his way between the herd, he found a highly attractive young woman in a corner, wiping blood from her foot. 'An wha are ye?' demanded the laird.

'Wha's askin?'

'A am the owner o these lands an the barn that ye are sittin in.'

'Weel ye micht tidy up the broken bottles aboot yer place; A cut masel' she said defiantly.

'Dinnae gie me ony o yer nonsense. Wha are ye?'

'Ma name is Nan Pollock.' She gave him a demure look, 'Whit's yer ain name?'

'Neer mind ma name. A am the Laird o Auchenskeith and ye are no welcome here, sae on yer wey. An yae last thing: A ken whit ye be. Suid ye decide tae visit yer cantrips on me again, we'll hae a banefire; an ye micht guess wha's banes'll be on it.' He raised a thumb and indicated she leave, and quickly. The woman rose and limped jauntily past the laird, brushing hard against him on the way.

That night as he lay on his bed, he could not get Nan Pollock out of his mind. She danced through his dreams, always taunting, always teasing, always alluring. He had to see her again. It was an unwise move by an otherwise wise man.

See her he did and he was drawn into her dark ways. It was a love-hate relationship based on deep passions. He secretly studied her books, learned spells and conjurations but always, to her annoyance, maintained a distance. In revenge she skimmed his milk so there was no butter, stopped his hens laying and had some of his cows running wild to the point of death. She was especially annoyed when he married. A year later his wife gave birth to a son and Nanny boldly marched up to the house and called out the laird and his wife saying that the boy was 'foirspokin' and was a gift to the Devil. The Lady of Auchenskeith, unaware of her husband's secret life, and horrified at the witch's presence, crossed herself and dropped to her knees in earnest prayer. The holy words were like acid on Nan's soul. Filled with dread, she lifted her skirts and ran. Auchenskeith set off after her raining down curses. As he caught up, she turned on him, 'Ye were mine. A gave ye ma heart an saul. A taught ye oor weys; bit ye were juist uisin me fer yer ain pleisur. Ye hae sawn an nou ye sall reap. Ye suppit wi the Deil an nor a lang spune did ye uise.' She spat at his feet, turned and stomped off.

THE WARLOCK LAIRD O AUCHENSKEITH

The Laird of Auchenskeith was out and about at first light inspecting his lands. It was time for harvest, and he was examining the fields to see in which order they should be scythed. As he rode along a track beside one of the larger fields, he noticed an aged man upon a stick, limping towards him. As they passed, the stranger raised the stick and hailed him, 'Guid mornin tae ye sir. Grand day fer the hairst.'

'Aye, it is,' said the laird, noticing how unusual was the man's staff, 'An that's a fine stick ye hae in yer haun.'

'Aye a hae hud it a wheen o years. It has served me weel an been the source o aa ma guid luck,'

The laird laughed, for he had taken a particular interest in glamourie and was intrigued. 'A cuid dae wi a wee bit o that masel.'

The man held the handle up to the laird's face, 'Interestin, is it no?'

The laird looked closely at the finely carved top. It was a gallimaufrey of magic: heads of witches, goblins, devils, cats and toads. It held his fascination. 'Hou much wuid ye ask fer it?'

'Ten years o yer life,' said the stranger with a laugh, as if he were joking.

The laird looked at the honest, kindly but simple face of the old man and thought to humour him. 'A thocht mebbe ten bawbees, but ten years o ma life is a high price.'

The stranger raised the stick and thrashed the ground three times. In an instant a band of horses and carts drew up and on the carts was the entire harvest for the laird's estates. 'Wow!' he exclaimed. 'That is vaudie. Houeer, a still hae tae shill it.'

No sooner said than done. The stick thrashed the ground three more times and the carters leaped down, flails in hand, and set about threshing and bagging the corn. Less than hour and the entire crop was done and on its way to the laird's mill.

Intrigued and impressed with what had just occurred, the laird looked at the old man and said, 'Mak the deal.'

The old man walked over to an ancient windblown hawthorn tree and broke off a dead twig. He brought it back to the laird, who had climbed down from his horse. The old man then pricked his thumb and handed the twig to the laird who did the same. They pressed bloody thumbs together and the deal was done. The stick was handed over and the laird held it up and examined again the fine carving. He looked across his harvested fields and was giddy with excitement. He turned to thank the stranger, but he was nowhere to be seen. A moment later Nan Pollock appeared. The laird had previously condemned her as a witch but had been gradually enthralled by her and attracted to her ways. 'Ye ken wha that wis, sir?'

'Yin o the fairy folk, a presume.'

'Yer gyte man; It wis nane ither than the Deil hissel.'

The laird laughed, 'Awa wi ye Nan. Ye are guid wi the yirbs an aa but little ye ken o the warl. The Deil wuidnae tak a conceat tae the likes o me.'

Nan gave a little nod of of her head. 'Mebbes aye, mebbes naw,' and went on her way.

The laird looked again at the stick and a little shudder ran through him.

True to the old man's prophecy, the laird had a rich and successful life and wanted for nothing. But time wears all and one night as he rose from his chair, he gave a groan. 'Ma auld banes are sair. A think the guid Lord will be caain on me suin.'

'Awa wi ye man,' said his wife, 'Ye hae at least anither ten years in ye.' She found him the next morning, quite dead.

Some say that in fact the Deil came to claim him and he disappeared down the heugh at the Walcat Holes in a flaught o fire and that he has been seen riding past Auchentiber in the company of the fairy folk

While these are folktales and one might assume that the Laird of Auchenskeith was fictional, when Bessie Dunlop was being tried for witchcraft, she claimed that she had seen the Laird, in the company of the Fairy Folk, riding into a loch near Edinburgh nine years after his death. There appear to be gaps in the tales that have, presumably lost in time.

38

Laird o Linn and Jack o the Scales

When he was barely a man, the Laird o Linn's father died. He had left a decent patrimony or inheritance of the estate and a conservative sum of money. No doubt he was expected to make the money make money rather than spend it. But young men, with a glowing sense of immortality, often assume that tomorrow will take care of itself and tend to profligacy, or reckless spending. In none-too-short a time the money was largely gone, and he resorted to borrowing. It so happened that the person who aided and abetted his spending was Jock o the Scales, the former gamekeeper to his father. In the guise of helping Jock and his wife he ran errands for the boy, pocketing much of the money in the process. With their general meanness and criminality, they amassed a not-inconsiderable sum of money. Then the fateful day came that he could not honour his debtors, chief of which was the guileful and insidious Jock o the Scales. Jock and his wife, with faces full of sympathy and hearts full of greed, offered to save him from the debtors' prison by taking the estate off of his hands. The price was a tenth of its worth, but the distraught young man agreed, and the papers signed.

With nothing more than the clothes he wore and a pocket of loose change, he decided that life was not worth living. He paid the house a last visit taking only a small wooden box with a few mementoes of his mother and father. He went to the local hostelry and sat nursing a pint of ale bought with his last few pence. As he sat in a darkened corner, he opened the box and from it removed a small key. Round it was wrapped a note of paper. He uncoiled the small sheet and read the message, 'My son, when aa things fail ye gang up tae Coal-heugh-glen, an this wee key wull get ye there a freen.' Fraught with sadness, but intrigued, he left the hostelry and made his way to where his father had indicated. In the thickest part of the tree-laid glen he found a tiny thatched cottage that was beyond repair. When he tried the key in the lock it wouldn't budge, but the timbers of the door were so old they fell in with a hard push. Inside he tore open the shutters and with the light from door and window saw, to his horror, a stool below a hangman's rope which was attached to a hook in the lath and plaster ceiling. On a support beam on top of the wall was chalked the message, 'Yer last freen.'

On the one hand it seemed like a black joke, on the other, the reality of existence. He decided that the latter was his only option. He stepped on to the rickety stool and placed the noose about his neck, then with a kick of the stool stepped into the air. In his mind he stepped into another world of blinding truth. It was a mere instant but yet seemed ageless and eternal: the way his so-called friends had played on his naivete and lack of worldly understanding to manipulate and defraud him. Now he understood, but it was too late he was about to be strangled into eternity. He could feel himself falling, but with an abrupt crash he hit the floor, for instead of strangling him, the rope along the hook and a lump of plaster fell striking him on the head. As he sat, nursing the bump on his head, he saw an envelope pasted to the top of the plaster. Opening it he found a note in his father's hand, 'Gang tae the richt back corner an ye'll fin twa loose stanes. Puu them oot and ye'll fin enough gowd an siller tae sort oot yer life. Be warned an be wise an lairn bi yer mistakes.' The lad removed the stones and found near a king's ransom in two small kists. He removed them, filled his pockets with enough as would cover his plans the replaced the kists and the stones so that it looked as before. He would collect it at a more suitable time.

The young Laird o Linn did indeed take his father's words to heart and sought to redress the wrongs of the past. Firstly, he continued as if he was in penury and borrowed a few pence here and there to cover food and lodgings. Noting those who gave of kindness and those who expected it back with interest. On a Friday night he went to the hostelry knowing that Jock o the Scales and his wife would be there with other accomplices. As he entered Jock called out, 'It's Yer Majesty come to beg borrow or steal. Whit will it be?'

The now former Laird o Linn smiled a weak smile, 'A wis hopin ye wuid help wi a wee bite tae eat.'

'Oh, is that no a shame,' said Jock's wife. The lad is stervin and we hae meat an meal eneugh tae gie awa.' There was all round mirth. Jock tore off a chunk of bread and handed it to the boy.

The lad took it and bit off a piece, 'That's kind o ye Jock.'

'That's me,' said Jock, 'Aa hert.' Laughter resounded round the room.

'True,' said the young man an wan day a hope tae reward ye bi buying back ma auld hoose makin suir ye get a guid profit.' There was a moment's silence of disbelief then the place erupted in raucous laughter.

'Tell ye whit,' said Jock, 'When ye get the money come an a'll sell it tae ye fer the same price a bocht it and whit's mair I'll gie ye back forty merks.'

'Really?' said young Linn, sounding his most gullible.

'Really,' said Jock.

'We suid wat thooms on it.' The expression on the young man's face was pure naivete.

'Indeed we suid,' said Jock as the company suppressed their laughter.

Jock ceremoniously spat on his thumb as did the young man. The thumbs were then pressed together. 'Ye are aa witnesses tae this contract?' said the laird. The company nodded in mock seriousness. At this point the young man pulled a purse from his pocket opened it and poured gold and silver coins on to the table. 'I think ye'll fin that the richt amount is there. Oh, except for forty merks, which a sall tak back. 'He stood up and looked at Jock and his wife, 'Ma cousin is juist back fae the continental wars and he an a troop o dragoons are but half a mile doon the road. Gin yer no oot o the hoose bi aucht o the clock, the morn's mornin, ye will be evicted forcefully.'

The place was in an uproar. Jock protested, 'Ye cannae dae this?'

'It is duin. Ye were a faus freen, an a hae speired aboot an fand that ye defraudit me mair than yince. Ye shawed me nae mercy, noo ye will reap whit ye sowed. An aa the rest o ye that did the same; a ken wha ye are and a'll mak siccar ye mak guid.'

True to his word the Laird o Linn took back his home and had Jock o the Scales and his wife drummed out of the district. He ensured that the others made good by good works for the church. Most importantly, for himself, though he was the richest man about, he always acted with charity on those in need and ensured that they were assisted. He was a champion of fair play and supported those whom he felt had been used and abused. He did indeed, as his father hoped, learn from the mistakes of the past.

39
Legend of Sawney Bean

'A'm seek an tired o diggin they bluidy ditches, faither,' said the young man, throwing his spade down.

'Ye'll bluidy well get oan wi it boy and earn yer keep.'

'A'm meant fer better things than this.'

'Aye, the puir's hoose, that's whit. Noo get oan wi it.' The older man picked up the spade and threw it in his son's direction.

It somersaulted and hit the lad on the leg, he grabbed it in anger, 'Ye auld bastart,' he raged, and swung at his father's head with the spade.

The older man nimbly lifted his own spade and warded off the blow, though the impact sent him sprawling in the ditch. The boy's spade flew over his head missing it by an inch. 'Ye wuid try an kill yer ain faither.'

'Aye, an mair besides, if needs be. I'm bound fer better things,' the son said and walked off.

'Bound fer the gallows, mair like it,' said his father.

'Hah!' was the reply.

Alexander Bain, always known as Sawney, young, fearless, sure of his own value and dangerously psychotic, took the twelve-mile road to Edinburgh. He went immediately to the Grassmarket in the hope of picking up some employment in the city. He arrived on the day of the Horse Fair. The market was full-to-bursting with row upon row of hundreds of hunters, cobs, shires, ponies and all colour and size of beast. The roar of the crowd was deafening, punctuated by snickers and screams from the horses. Occasionally one horse would take objection to another and bite or buck. Sawney loved it. He squeezed his way through the throng until his eyes set upon a woman strutting along, apparently oblivious to the lewd remarks of the traders. Sawney edged between the horses to get closer. He was a few yards behind when a dealer grabbed her by the arm and said something close to her ear.

She spun and slapped him hard across the left cheek. He looked at her in amazement, put a hand to his severely reddened face than made to swing the other fist at her. Sawney grabbed the arm and felled the man with one blow. Instantly his eyes filled with demon hate at all about him, challenging them to defend their man. Seeing his labourer's muscles and crazed look they turned away laughing. The woman looked him up and down, 'If ye want thanks, ye can bugger off. A can haunle masel.'

'I hae nae doot, 'said Sawney, 'A dinnae want thanks, A juist fanciet a fecht.'

'A man efter ma ain hert,' she said, then turned and walked away.

Sawney watched her disappear into the crowd, thought better of her getting away and strode after. He caught up on the bend of the West Bow, 'Wuid ye fancy a drink?'

'Aye a fancy a drink,' she replied and strode on.'

Unsure whether that was an acceptance or not, he swerved round an oncoming pedestrian and walked beside her, 'Hoo aboot twae?'

'Keep coontin,' she replied.

They found a suitably boisterous hostelry and ordered two stoups of ale, 'Whit is yer name?' asked Sawney.

'Agnes, Agnes Douglas,' she said, 'An ye?'

'Sawney, Sawney Bain.' The stoups arrived and both took a drink, 'Whit did that gomeril say tae ye?'

'He said a wis a hure, when I am in fact a wanweirdit lady.'

'So a hure, then.'

'Aye!' They both burst into laughter. When they had stilled, she asked, 'Whit dae ye dae?'

'It's no whit a dae, it's whit a'm gaun tae dae.'

'Whit's that?'

'A'm gaun tae leeve lik a king.'

'Hou wull ye dae that?'

'Same as a king, a'll leeve aff the work o ithers.'

'But hou?'

'Same as a king, I'll steal it; wi force if necessar.'

'Ye'll hing frae the scaffold in the Gressmercat.'

'No! a'm awa tae Carrick in Gallawa. I've heard the folk there are the wildest aboot, sae a'll be richt at hame.' He leaned forward conspiratorialy, 'Wuid ye like tae be ma queen?'

'Aye!'

And so it was that Alexander Bain and Agnes Douglas set out on the road to infamy.

***

Out of the Lothians and into shire of Lanark they travelled, on over the Clyde past the stronghold of the Douglases to the source of the River Ayr. Once past Cumnock they arrived in the lands of the Kennedies. They passed from the River Doon into the valley of the Girvan which they crossed near Threave. Soon they were experiencing extreme hunger pangs as they found little among the hovels that people lived in. In one small hamlet they had been set upon by locals with their dogs and chased as thieving tinkers and gypsies. Ahead of them was the stronghold of the Fergusons at Kilkerran, which they thought to avoid for fear of more of the same. They decided to go up the slopes of Cairn Hill.

The moor was open but covered in scrub and long heather, which was hard going and exacerbated their plight. They struggled down the sides of a steep, enchanting glen, which they cursed for its hindrance. They climbed the almost perpendicular opposite side and up out over the rim. Suddenly Sawney dropped flat and indicated for Agnes to do the same. She bellied forward to him. 'Whit is it?'

'There's somebody aheid.' He rose up slowly on his arms to get a better view, Agnes did the same. In front was a barefoot boy of about twelve years in a linen shirt and short breeks. He was sitting on a large rock, a thin pole leaning against his shoulder. Grazing nearby were five hobbled, small black hairy cows. The boy was eating a large bannock and cheese. Sawney turned to Agnes, at the same time putting his fingers to his mouth. She nodded. He then pointed a finger at her and then at the boy. She nodded again and rose to her feet and strolled towards the lad. He turned and looked towards her then looked about, as if looking for others. 'Mornin,' she said.

He stared at her, his bottom lip hanging, saying nothing in return. 'That's a bonnie bannock ye hae there. Wid ye be up fer sharin a bittie?'

'It's ma denner,' said the boy.

'Aye, bit it's Christian tae share.' He just continued staring, so after a quick glance about, she lifted a leg and placed a foot on the rock slipping it beneath his thigh, she then hiked up her skirt to the knee, 'A cuid gie ye somethin in return.'

The boy looked at the long lean muscular legs in amazement then up at Agnes, 'It's ma denner.'

'Weel it's mine noo,' she said, her face now corrupted with malice and fury. She grabbed the boy by the hair and hauled him off the rock. He started to howl, which startled the cows. In a moment she had him on the ground and strangling the life from him. The boy thrashed and kicked and was on the point of breaking free when Sawney arrived and stabbed him clean through the heart. The lads mouth opened wide, gurgled, then he gave a long slow exhalation and lay, eyes wide to the sky.

Agnes rolled over on to her back beside the body, 'Get me a bit o that cheese Sawney, wuid ye?'

Sawney rose up, looked about then began to gather up the food that now lay scattered. He handed pieces to Agnes then sat beside her eating his own. They quickly finished their meal and Sawney rose to his feet 'I'll fling his body in the glen.' He grabbed the boy by the wrist and began to drag him, face down, towards the drop. As he did so the boy's breeks were dragged off exposing his lower half. Agnes followed, gathering up the discarded garment on the way. She couldn't take her eyes off the small perfectly formed buttocks of the lad and involuntarily licked her lips, 'Sawney,' she said, 'Dae me a favour.'

'Whit's that?'

'Afore ye howk that thing ower the heugh, cut me aff a side o beef.'

'Whit?'

She pointed to the body, 'There's nae point in haein aa that guid meat gaun tae waste.'

He stared at her, a momentary a look of disbelief on his face, then to the boy, 'Ye ken, a wuidnae hae thocht o daein that, but noo that ye mention it, it maks guid sense.' Without hesitation at the sacrilege he was performing, Sawney dutifully sliced flesh from bone, he then hurled the bloody cadaver over the drop.

Later in the day they found a secluded spot beside a burn with a small, dead rowan tree. They lit a fire and roasted the flesh on wooden skewers. As the meat sizzled and cooked Sawney turned to Agnes, a grin wide on his face, 'That smells grand.'

'Aye it does!' she agreed.

After ravenously tearing into their gruesome meal, they collapsed side by side satisfied. 'That was juist grand.' said Agnes to the sky.

Sawney breathed in deeply through his nostrils and patted his stomach., 'Aye it wis; probably the best meat a hae tastit.' He burped loudly, 'An there's plenty mair hereaboots.'

***

'Why can we no come wi ye?' said the young girl.

'Because ye're a lassie and killin is man's wark.'

'Granny killt loads o folk.'

'Aye, bit she's Granny an no ye,' he said stabbing a finger at her, 'Juist get on wi cleanin thae buits.'

'A suild put them oan an gie ye a kick up the erse.'

The boy picked up the severed head that sat on the rock and swung it at the girl,' she ducked, spat at him and ran out past the dismembered limbs that were being smoked for preservation from the roof of the cave. The tide was just on its way out and time for the clan to prepare for their day's ambush.

The Bain clan's cave was at Bennane Heid two miles north of the mouth of the River Stinchar. The nearest settlement was Kirkcudbrycht Innertig, two miles up the Stinchar. In those lawless times, along with Galloway, Carrick was its own wild place. It was ruled ruthlessly by the Kennedys but they, apart from taxing, cared little for its people or their fate – unless, of course, it affected taxes. In times past the sea and the shoreline were the main arteries of migration and trade. This served the Bains very well. It was not long after their arrival that Sawney and Agnes found the cave and set up business. From high up on Bennane they would split up, one going north and one south. Whoever saw someone coming would check there were no other travellers behind then run to the other and warn them; an ambush was then set. The easiest way was to pose as travellers and engage the unwitting victim in conversation, then with speed and force they would slash the jugular vein and let the person bleed to death. Sawney thought that it made the meat taste better and, apart from some blood to clean off, it ensured the clothing was not badly damaged: it could easily be washed in the burn. Over many years lone travellers would disappear, even couples. With a good source of food and a steady income from the stolen valuables, they prospered. When it came to dispose of valuables, especially for whisky, Sawney and Agnes were wily enough and ensured that they travelled all the way up to the Royal Burgh of Ayr to sell them at the mercat or south to Portpatrick to catch travellers coming from or going to Ireland. Well-off and healthier than most, they began to have children, lots of them: fourteen to be precise. In time the sons and daughters had children, by each other … and Sawney. The clan finally numbered forty-eight.

As large a clan and inbred as they were, they thrived on their ill-gotten gains and unholy fare. For twenty-five-years they, with evil intelligence and guile, killed with impunity. No one could be certain why people disappeared, but the rumour was that it was the owners of hostelries. The rumours grew so bad that some were attacked, and many gave up their businesses and moved elsewhere. Rumour also said that a thousand had vanished, but people exaggerate, though there is no doubt it was many hundreds. Because of their cunning, it looked like the reign of terror would never end.

***

Sawney lay on the grass beside Agnes proudly watching their hunters depart. The road had been quiet for nearly a week, and apart from dried and smoked fare, they had no fresh meat. 'Ye ken,' he said, 'Years ago a fella asked me a question a hae whyles pondered oan. He asked me what was worse, tae kill ae man or tae kill ten. A said ten. He said it wis worse tae kill yin, because aince ye kill yin, it easy tae kill the ither nine.' He sucked in air through his two front teeth, 'Ye ken, a noo think he wis richt. A didnae enjoy the first; but I've enjoyed the rest.

Agnes sat up and looked at him, 'Whit dae ye mean ye didnae enjoy the first. Ye said it was the best meat ye had ever tastit.'

'Aye richt eneuch.' They both laughed.

The Bain's had a clear strategy. Always keep lookout; never let anyone escape or go, change locations for ambushes, leave the locals alone and, lastly, avoid people on horseback.

The hunters consisted of eight sons and eight grandsons. The youngest was aged just nine, but already a seasoned killer. Sawney had said they should trek down towards Glenapp as they hadn't been there for a while. The troop headed south along the shore, the youngest running ahead to warn of people. His long lean muscular legs carried him two hundred yards ahead. As he came around an outcrop, he stopped dead. Heading north were a couple mounted on tall hunters. They were loaded for a long journey, and even at the distance he could see they were obviously wealthy. He spun on his heel, raced back and reported to Sawney's eldest son, Saw. 'Ye ken, a dinnae fancy a lang trek the day. We'll juist tak these twa,' he said.

'Bit Saw, they're oan horses. We dinnae dae horses, said his young brother-nephew.

'We dae noo,' said Saw, with a primeval growl in his voice, 'Up the bank and get spread oot.'

With animal efficiency they followed each other up the near vertical incline and spread out four-aside among the thick heather along the road. Two headed north to start walking as travellers. They gauged it so they would pass the riders where the other were hiding. At the last moment the pair would create a distraction. The riders on the big horses made slow progress up the hill so the two killers stopped and seemed to be having a discussion. They then gave each other a push and continued towards their victims. As the riders approached the gauntlet the pair began to shout and fight each other. They riders came on, but more slowly, as expected. What was not expected was the man, a former soldier, put his hand to his sword hilt. The fighters stopped suddenly and ran to grab the reins of the horses. The horse of the woman was caught, but as the assailant was about to grab the man's, he drew his sword and slashed the attacker's shoulder. At the same time the others were out of hiding and running at the couple. The soldier's horse took fright, but instead of fleeing he kicked out and nearly disembowelled a Bain. The soldier slashed and the horse bucked and kicked so that no one dare go too close. The luckless woman was dragged from her horse and her throat cut. At the same time her clothes were hauled off her. For good measure, and anger at their brothers' injuries, they slashed open her stomach, so her entrails slipped out. Still alive, she looked on in despairing horror at her fate. Meanwhile, the soldier, seeing the fate of his companion and still mounted, gave his horse a hard slap with the flat of his blade and the great beast took off in a fury and thundered northwards, disappearing over the brow of the hill.

'A telt ye Saw. That's hou we dinnae dae horses.'

'Saw looked at his brother then swung a brutal slap that sent the boy careering away and falling over. He then turned to his siblings. 'Ony o ye mention a word o this tae Sawney an I'll kill ye, juist afore he does me. We'll tak the woman's horse and set it free up the Stinchar. Tak the gear aff it an hide it an the body till we cam back.' Saw then went to his wounded brothers. Malcom, with the slashed shoulder, said he was fine but he would stay and look after Walter, who was still doubled up with pain. They would hide among the heather on the hill above and wait for their return. The rest then set out on the road to Glenapp.

The soldier had, meanwhile, ridden hard for Turnberry. He had heard that King James II was touring the lands of Cunningham, Kyle and Carrick which he had held in regality as a prince - an ideal way of filling his coffers. The soldier reasoned that King James would oblige in hunting down these brigands to raise his prestige. Not only that, he would have a troop of seasoned warriors with him. As luck would have it, a vanguard of the king's troop had arrived at Turnberry to warn of James's arrival. The soldier alerted them to the attack and the captain promised to inform the king as soon as he arrived the next day.

In the Bain's cave the atmosphere was thick with tension. For rather than saying what had occurred and abandoning their home, they said nothing. They knew if their father had an inkling of what had happened, he would go wild and perhaps even kill his eldest son. His law was the law, never to be broken on pain of death, for it had kept them from harm for twenty-five years. The trip to Glenapp had been a success and they had returned with a pouchful of merks as well as the corpse of the female rider. Sawney took no notice of their arrival, so used was he to it and did not inquire of events. Life and death carried on as normal: at least for a few days.

At last King James arrived at Turnberry with his retinue and a troop of soldiers. The captain of the vanguard reported on the state of Turnberry for his arrival and added that the mysterious disappearances of people in his regality of Carrick might now have an explanation. After supper the soldier was given an audience and the king offered the services of himself and the troop, if the soldier would kindly take them to the scene of the atrocity the following day.

After a leisurely breakfast the king ordered up his troop of four hundred and two bloodhounds were brought from Cullane to aid the search. The journey took a little over two hours. At first the soldier could not place the precise spot, but a bloodhound soon found the bloodstained grasses. The dog-handler kept the dogs silent as they traced the trail down to the shore. Wisely, the king sent ten of the troop south of the headland and ten to the north to cut off any escape along the shore as it was now low tide. A mounted cohort remained on the track while the rest made their way down the steep slope.

As soldiers, led by the dogs, their handler and the king, swarmed down the headland, the Bains, hearing the commotion about them, retreated into their cave in fear. They were attackers and had never been challenged - they had no idea how to respond. The captain of the guard was ordered to enter with ten men. A torch, found at the entrance was lit, and, swords drawn, they entered. The first thing that greeted them was the sweet smell of cooking.

'I think we hae got them at their denner,' said the captain to no one in particular.

'Smell's guid,' said the sergeant behind him.

'Aye,' said another, 'A huvnae had a decent plate o meat fer weeks.'

As they moved deeper in, one soldier looked up and exclaimed, 'God in Heaven preserve us.'

As they all looked up, they immediately crossed themselves. Toughened veterans who had fought in France alongside Joan of Arc felt a chill of demonic evil run through them at the sight of preserved limbs hanging from the roof and on high ledges of the cave. The captain called for more troops to enter with firebrands. Soon the place was lit as they moved deeper into the cave system. The first encounter was with three young women huddled in a recess, their eyes wide with fear. Further in were boys and girls from teenagers to early twenties. Instead of offering up resistance they were cowed and obeisant and when ordered out they flinched and whimpered like beaten dogs. The captain continued until he came to a large open space, strewn with rush and heather, over which lay a thick layer of plaids. All around were boxes of jewellery, coins, fine dresses and doublets, and the spoils of savagery. Lying atop them was Sawney and Agnes all dressed in absurd finery like a child after it raids its parents' wardrobes. The captain looked at them in disgust, turned about and ordered his sergeant to bring in the king. Sawney lay back, his fingers knotted behind his head, a look of self-satisfaction on his face. Agnes sprawled out, her head resting on Sawney's broad chest. She wore a similar expression. The king entered, a scented handkerchief over his nose. He was noticeably disturbed by what lay before and about him. Sawney cocked his head and grinned, 'Weel, weel, a meetin o kings. Welcome tae the seat o ma wee humble kingdom. The king looked away in revulsion. 'Aye ye may weel show disgust, but we are no sae unalike. Ye ride aboot this land wi yer mounted henchmen trampin doon onybody that threatens yer robbery o the work o ithers. Wi that money ye ride intae ither lands murderin an pillaging bringin daith tae ordnar fowk fer yer gratification and power. Ye enrich yersel aff the back o ithers. Ye dinnae eat their flesh, but ye micht as weel, fer the result is the same. Hypocrite!' The last word was spat out with fury.

The king turned about, 'Tak them tae the Gressmercatt in Edinburgh and execute the damnable lot o them.' He paused a moment, 'But no until a gie the order. A will no hae this devilry in ma kingdom.' He looked back into the space a moment, 'Hae aa the valuables pit on a cairt an taen to Edinburgh Castle.'

'Hah!' shouted Sawney, 'Still thieving yersel.' A soldier shoved a sword into his mouth smashing teeth and splitting it wide open, 'A'll hae mair tae say.' He slobbered, spitting teeth and blood.

Among the chaos of goods, shirts were found and ripped to tie up the band. Ropes were also found and tied about their necks, tethering them in groups separated by sex and age. Walter, unable to walk, was mounted on a travois and Saw ordered to drag him. Apart from water and a little bread to ensure their arrival in the capital, they had to walk the hundred miles. Their reputation preceded them, and, on the way, they were pelted with all manner of disgusting material. The soldiers warned, on the king's orders, against stones as he wanted them in Edinburgh in one piece for execution.

The journey took a week. As the younger ones collapsed, carts were commandeered to carry them. The rest were whipped on. On their arrival at the Grassmarket they were corralled in livestock pens, chains were found to shackle them and a contingent of soldiers set to guard them night and day until the king, who was still on business, returned. Crowds grew daily to ogle at this detritus of inhumanity. People were again warned against throwing stones and especially dung as a soldier had been hit and the culprit almost found himself spiked. Rotten vegetables were used instead, which the Bains, on the brink of starvation, eagerly consumed. That was banned too.

After ten days, the king arrived back in the city and the order was put out for execution the following day.

A dais was quickly set up for the royal party near the pens for King James and Queen Joan. In front of the pens was placed a large solid table and at the bottom side of the Grassmarket, built over the past week, a very large bonfire. The Bains watched the rising pile of wood knowing fully what awaited them, yet they bore it with, for the troops, an unnerving fatalism, even joking, 'Haw sodger! Is that whaur the king is gaun tae dine on the banes o the Bains?' called Saw, and the clan erupted into uproarious laughter.

'Ye'll no be lauchin when they spit-roast ye, ya trash o Hell,' was the reply.

The Bain's laughed louder.

The king and queen arrived just after dinner and settled on their thrones, to the approval of the baying crowd. Blood lust was up, and the people wanted plenty of it. The Provost stood up on the dais and called out the king's proclamation:

> It is his majesty's desire that acause o the heinous an barbaric practices by this devilish clan that nae mercy be gien and nae quarter offerit. That they hae forfeitit the richt tae a fair and just trial. It is the judgement of Good King James that the men will be emasculated and their hauns an feet be dismemberit frae their bodies and bled until deid. That their bodies sall be consignit tae the flames. That the womenfolk are guilty of abominations and witchcraft an sall be assignit tae the flames. In the name of the Father, the Son and the Holy Spirit, Amen.

The soldiers went into the pens, swords at the ready and hauled the chained men and boys out into the open. The women and girls were then dragged out and tied along the timber fencing. Missiles were hurled and the crowd began to surge forward. The soldiers levelled spears and some screamed as they were pushed on to the points.

The soldiers moved in to grab the youngest boy, but there was a roar of disapproval from the crowd, so they made a grab at Saw, who had given them continual grief on the road. He was dragged to the table and stripped. The executioner and his assistants went to work with chopper and knife and the deed was done. Saw was thrown on the ground, a bloody, writhing screaming entity. The crowd were ecstatic as one-by-one the Bains went into the hands of the royal killer and lost theirs, and else besides.

Sawney, the last to be amputated, called out, as his life blood drained away, 'It is not over. It will never be over.'

The bodies, some still in their death agonies, were dragged to the bonfire and thrown into the flames. All the time the women watched in horror at the bloody deeds done to their menfolk. Then one by one they were dragged, screaming curses on all the world, towards the conflagration. They were unceremoniously thrown on. Only Agnes, now small lean and gaunt, managed to momentarily break free and rush towards the crowd, who retreated in panic, 'If ye but tastit the flesh I hae tastit, I widnae been here noo,' she screamed. As the soldiers grabbed her. she scratched, bit and fought like a fury. Two burly soldiers grabbed her arms from out the melee and threw her headlong onto the fire. There was a gasp as she seemed, for a moment to fly over the flames, then she plunged into the furnace sending up showers of sparks.

As the smoke rose high up over the castle the wind changed and sent clouds of reek up the Grassmarket. Within it was the unmistakeable smell of sweet, cooked flesh. The king was glad he had just eaten, for he, along with much of the crowd, found it difficult to stop the saliva forming in his mouth.

In regality or in liberam regalitatum in old Scots law, was land held by the king and came under different laws from the rest of the kingdom. The lord assigned to run it, similar to a sheriff, was responsible only to the king himself. Ayrshire was held in regality to King James. Along with royal burghs and burghs of regality they were a way to fill the royal coffers.

40

The year was 1698 and part the way through the Seven Ill Years or Starvation Times that had struck Scotland. This was through a combination of protectionist trading by the French, changes in the cattle trade and a succession of failed harvests. People left the countryside in droves for towns and cities and many hundreds, even thousands, died. There were some who, through knowledge of the land and its bounty, survived.

Jock and Jean ambled down the old Carrick drove road by way of Mackailston and Cloyntie. As they struggled up the track towards Blair, Jean stopped and dropped the straps of her travois, 'A'm seek o haulin aa oor gear aboot the kintraside Jock. A cannae dae it ony mair.'

'Fegs woman,' said Jock, 'we're traivellin folk and that's whit we dae: traivel.'

'A ken John,' said Jean, a quavering hurt in her voice, 'bit ma banes are ower sair and I canne lie ahint anither dyke. I want a hame: a hoose o ma ain.'

'C'mon lass we'll be at Little Egypt bi suppertime.'

'Suppertime? Man wur hungert, an scarce a bite tae eat. We're in starvation times; the hale kintra is stervin.'

'Then we'll gang an see the meenister at the Barr; he aye has a pickle meal tae spare fer folks.'

Reluctantly, Jean lifted the straps over her shoulders and staggered on behind her man, muttering that he should have gone by Kilkerran as there were less hills. 'That's acause a'm gaun tae dae a wee bit guddlin,' he called back in response.

They stopped at the burn running into the Stinchar at North Balloch and, while a tired-out Jean set a fire going and gathered dandelion leaves, nettle-tops and garlic mustard, Jock hand-caught two large trout. After eating one apiece with their wild salad they continued the remaining five miles to the

Barr. At the manse Jean kissed her fingers then knocked on the sturdy door, then kissed her fingers again, not for luck but at the pain from the solid unforgiving wood. A young woman dressed in servant's clothes answered the knock, 'Aye?' she enquired.

'Eh, we've cam tae see the meenister and get his blessins,' said Jean.

'Is that aa?' said the lass, raising an eyebrow.

Drawing on years of living life on the edge, Jean summoned up a face of childlike innocence, 'Whit else wid there be?'

The girl gave a wry smile, 'I'll juist see if the meenister can see ye.'

The maid came back a moment later and ushered them into the withdrawing room, 'Juist staun there and dinnae ye dare sit on the furnitur.' She left the room leaving the door ajar.

A moment later the minister entered. Realising he still had on his bonnet, Jock quickly removed it and half bowed, Jean made an attempt at a curtsey. The minister smiled, shook both their hands, referencing their names as he did so. He then bade them sit on the upright chairs by the window while he stood with his back to the fire, hands clasped behind his back, 'Now, what can I do for you?'

'We juist cam tae get yer blessin, Sir.'

'That would be a pleasure Jean.' The minister held up his right hand and commended the blessing on the travellers, then added:

'Now, would you like a cup of tea? Some has just arrived at Girvan from the Indies.'

'That wuid be very nice Meenister, thank ye' said Jean, giving a look to Jock.

'Aye thank ye meenister, that wuid be awfy nice,' said Jock.

The minister pulled a cord at the side of the fire and within seconds the girl opened the door. She nodded and smiled at the cleric. 'Can you bring through a pot of tea for us, please, Jessie?'

'Yes sir, I have the kettle on already.'

A short while later she re-entered the room with a tray on which was a teapot and three china bowls. The minister looked at the old couple and did not fail to miss the look of disappointment on their faces. 'Perhaps you could fetch through some of your lovely buttered scones as well, Jessie.'

'Have you tried tea?' said the minister. It's said to be grand for the constitution. A wee bit bitter, but if you add a wee drop of sugar it makes it quite palatable. Neither Jock nor Jean had any idea what he was talking about with his 'fancy Southron talk'.

The reverend poured the green liquid into the three bowls, added a liberal spoonful of sugar to each and stirred. 'It's a wee bit too hot at the moment, but if you give it a few minutes it'll be fine.'

Jean looked at the steaming bowls then to the cleric, 'Ye ken meenister, I've aye hud a hankerin tae leeve the wey ye dae: a hoose, wi a gran fire and bakin scones an sic like. Bit Jock here says a'm daft and that we suid trauchle the roads fer aye. A'm gettin too auld an a wuid like a hoose o ma ain.'

Jock looked hard at Jean then to the minister, 'Tell her sir, there's nae wey fowks lik us wuid get a hoose. A mean tae say, wha wuid gie a hoose tae traivelin fowk.' Jean sat bolt upright, her face red with anger.

The minister saw the argument brewing and sought to calm the situation, 'Hold on, hold on! A few folks have left the strath and gone to Ayr or Girvan to seek work. There are deserted cots about here; most are owned by the laird, but there is one on the far side of the glebe that you could have. It needs a little repair but is mainly wind and water-tight. Try it and see how you like it.'

Jock gave a great sigh, 'Aye fine, if it maks Jean happy.'

After having their first taste of tea, which they enjoyed more for the experience than the taste, and the scones for the taste more than the experience - as they dropped crumbs all over the floor - they set out for their new and first-time home.

The building was a single room, small, dry-stone structure with a thatched roof, two shuttered windows and a door, which scraped the ground as it opened. Inside was a ring of stones for the fire in the middle of the floor and in the corner was a bed made from a rough-hewn pallet covered in dry grass and heather. Jock opened the shutters on the window then went out to gather sticks for the fire while Jean threw herself down on the pallet and wriggled in pleasure.

Jock returned with a large bundle of wood and set about lighting a fire. The smoke spread out then rose up past the rafters and found its way to the hole mid-apex on the roof. Very soon the heat warmed the small space. Jock added a few more sticks and a large branch he had found beside the river then he went over and lay on the pallet beside his wife. 'Whit dae ye think, Hen?'

'Grand.' Jean paused a moment, 'But it's no quite richt.'

'Hou dae ye mean?'

'A dinnae ken, but it's juist no quite richt.'

They spent following day gathering new bedding and getting in piles of sticks for the fire.

That evening as they lay on their more comfortable bed in a warmed room Jock said, 'Hou's that noo, Hen?'

'Guid!' she paused as before, 'But it's no quite richt.'

'In whit wey, Hen?'

'Last nicht a cuidna see the sternies. Cuid ye tak aff a pickle theik fae the ruif?'

Jock rose from the bed and scrambled up the wall and began removing the thatch above Jean. 'Hou's that?

'A pickle mair,' she said. As he worked to remove it, she added, 'Juist tak it aa aff.'

The following night, as they lay looking up at the star-spangled heavens, Jean said, 'Whit a sicht Jock. A neer tire o it.'

'Aye Hen, it's juist perfit. Eh?'

'Guid John, but no quite richt.'

'Whit's no?' he said, his brows furrowing.

'A miss the wind on ma face. Cuid ye tak aff the shutters and the door?'

Jock rose again from the bed, took out the shutters and leaned them against the opposite wall from the bed, then lifted the door from it hinges and placed it by the shutters. He climbed back under the covers. 'Duin! Is that it?'

'Aye!'

Jock relaxed and gave a long exhale of breath.

'Nearly,' said Jean.

Jock sat bolt upright, 'Whit?' his voice was near a shriek.

'A said, nearly.'

'How nearly?' said Jock, his voice thick with sarcasm.

'There's nae need tae be lik that, John Cunninghame. A want it perfit and it's no quite; it's…' Jean gave her best pause, 'nearly.'

Jock sank back on the bed with a great sigh of exasperation. He gazed up into the heavens his head moving from side to side, 'Nearly!'

Next day Jock took his axe and went up the River Stinchar to gather more wood for the fire. He also took a cleek which he hung out of sight under his coat - if a salmon happened to make itself available, then Jock was not going to pass it by. Luck was with him, for not only did he manage to gather a large bundle of sticks and a ten-foot dead birch tree, he also hooked a salmon that he saw sliding under the riverbank. He gutted the fish, eating the heart, liver and kidney raw then wrapped the fish in some old linen and hung it from the armpit of his coat. As he walked, he could feel it slap against his breeks. The going was awkward with the fish, the sticks and the small tree, but necessity is also the mother of perseverance and after a few cuts and bruises to his hands and arms on the tree he reached the cot. Jean had been out foraging and had brought back a selection of leaves and flowers. Jock hid the fish behind the door while Jean boiled a cauldron of water. She then added the leaves and flowers before dropping the salmon in and covering it with a wooden lid. She then placed the vessel in a corner and threw an old woollen blanket over it. The fish would cook nicely in an hour without fishy odours to betray her man's poaching. She threw some garlic mustard leaves on the fire for good measure. They had both lived to a ripe old age of fifty without falling foul of the church or magistrates by always covering their tracks. As evening descended, they ate a satisfying meal of salmon and herbs, covered the cauldron again and retired to bed. Jock was just drifting off when Jean dug him in the ribs, 'A ken whit it is.'

Jock groaned, 'Whit's whit?'

'Whit's fashin me!'

A ken whit's fashin me,' said Jock, with irritable humour.

Jean pointed to the pink glow above the western gable of the house, 'Sindoon; a cannae see it. That waa's in the wey. Can ye push it doon?'

Jock got up and with his axe chopped both end of the birch tree until he had an eight-foot pole. With this he began toppling the gable.

'Can ye knock doon the ither yin so I can see the sin arisin.' She then waggled her finger in the direction of the door, 'An ye mey as weel tak doon the front yin so I can see the low winter sin.'

Jock laboured on until all three walls were demolished then climbed back into the bed that lay against the single remaining north wall. Jean looked about herself: the river, the dappled hills, the rosy glow of the setting sun and the faultless blue above her. As a soft, late-spring breeze played about her face she said, 'Perfit!'

41

Ma faither gied me a horse,	*gave*
An ma mither gied me a coo;	*cow*
Ma brither gied me a boar,	
An ma sister gied me a sou.	*sow*

Chorus

Oh its yin tae me	
Whether A mairry noo or no	*marry*
Mairry or tairry or bide as I be	*tarry/hold back, stay*

A got werk frae the horse.	*work*
An milk frae the coo,	
Bacon frae the boar,	
An piglets frae the sou.	

Chorus

Ma faither gied me a cockerel,
Ma mither gied me a hen,
Ma brither gied me a robin,
An ma sister gied me a wren.

Chorus

A got crawin fae the cockerel,
A got eggs fae the hen,
Whistlin fae the robin,
An chirpin fae the wren,

Chorus

Ma faither gied me a cat,
An ma mither gied me a moose, *mouse*
Ma brither gied ma a flae, *flea*
An ma sister gied me loose. *louse*

Chorus

A haed great fun
Watchin the cat chase the moose,
A got bitten bi the flae,
An scartin fae the loose. *scratching*

Oh its yin tae me
Whether A mairry no or noo
Mairry or tairry or bide as I be.

The song concerns a tocher or dowry which the girl has been given. Seeing she had done so well, she thinks that, perhaps, the single life is preferable.

42

Maggie Mollach and Broonie Clod

Maggie Mollach was a strange creature: small, skinny and wizened, even when young. Sometime in her early years she gave birth to a boy who had, according to the often-brutal attitudes of the time, the look of a brownie or broonie, a supernatural house elf. Unkindly, he was usually referred to as Broonie Clod, due to his awkward ways. Small and physically twisted as Maggie and Broonie were, they were also superb workers and many an Ayrshire farmer hired them to their benefit. However, one farmer found them so industrious that he fired his other workers. This upset Maggie so much that she played endless tricks on the farmer until he re-hired them. The farmer, though grateful of Maggie and her son's labour, feared and hated them, and when the clipping, carding and spinning of the wool was complete, he put about a rumour that she was a witch. Maggie and Broonie were forced to flee. They migrated north, doing casual work on the way, until they arrived at Fincastle Mill near Pitlochry. Here they took up residence in a tiny cottage with a flourmill beside and milled the local grain at a reasonable rate. With their great industry and fairness, locals ignored their looks and saw them for what they were: kind, social people. But not everyone saw them like that. One girl, who was about to be married, decided that she could, in the popular slang, 'tak a len o them.' She had, unwisely, not laid aside enough flour for her wedding cake, so she waited until the mill was closed for the night, entered it and, using the grain that Maggie and Broonie had taken as payment for their work, began to mill it into flour. At the same time, she put a pot of water to boil on to the fire for a hot drink. Maggie, being tired, had gone to bed and was sound asleep, but Broonie, hearing the wheels turning, went over to the mill to see what was happening. All he could see in the glow of the fire was a dark figure pouring grain into the hopper, 'Wha is there?' he called. There was no reply. 'Wha is there?' he called again.

'Mise mi fein.'

Unable to understand Gaelic, Broonie called again, 'Wha is there?'

Perthshire was on the border of the Highlands and Lowlands and most people had Gaelic and Scots, so she replied in translation 'Me masel.'

'Ye suidnae be workin oor mill. Tis no richt.'

In reply the girl lifted the pot of boiling water and threw it over Broonie. He screamed in agony and ran from the mill. He crashed through the door of the cottage, waking Maggie in the process. She lit a candle and looked at the hysterical Broonie. His face was livid, and the skin was blistering and beginning to slough off, 'Wha did this tae ye?' she yelled.

'Me masel! Twas me masel."

'Wis that no a daft thing tae dae tae yersel, ma wee tyke.' She said, half in annoyance and half in pity. She then tended the horrendous damage to his face and shoulders. In the deep hours of the night he began to fade, but not before he had described what he had seen in the mill. Maggie listened and a vengeful fury rose in her. She stilled her rage to care for her boy, but the pain was too much for wee Broonie and his heart gave out.

Distraught, she wrapped him in a winding sheet and carried his broken body into the woods. There, in a glade, glowing with the morning sun, she tore at the ground with her fingers and a stick until she had made a shallow grave. She then meticulously covered him over and replaced the turf so that there were no visible signs of the grave. Maggie then returned and continued her work at the mill. As well as the milling, in her spare hours she milked cows for local crofters. Few asked about Broonie, but when they did, she said he was lying down or unwell. She became aware of rumours that she had done away with him, but ignored them, biding her time. One morning she had no grain to mill so went to work at the croft of a man whose daughter had recently married. Maggie was leading the cow to a halter ring on the wall of the house when, through the open window, she heard the girl bragging to her mother how she had outwitted the creature at the mill. In her hand Maggie carried a small, but weighty, three-legged milking stool. She let go the cow and with all her might threw the stool through the window striking the girl on her forehead, killing her instantly. Not waiting to hear the consequences, Maggie rushed home removed her purse of earnings from the eaves of the cottage, bundled a few clothes and two precious pewter plates into a sheet and set off at haste southwards. At Perth she headed southwest past Stirling and Glasgow back to Ayrshire.

In time she reached Kilmarnock and found work carding and spinning. In the workloft with the other lasses, she would often suggest roots and herbs that might cure or help with a cold, a rash, a boil and the like. As many of her simple country cures worked, she soon had a stream of people to her door. Inevitably the church and authorities took an interest, but not with any benign intent. With her crooked form and grizzled features Maggie looked, to all intents, like a witch. She was hauled before the local magistrate and found guilty of practising witchcraft. The ultimate sentence was applied: she would be taken to a place of execution, strangled and then burned to ashes.

On the appointed day, Maggie was hauled from prison and unceremoniously dragged to her fate. She was shoved on to the logs, peats, tar and tinder, then tied to the stake. The hooded executioner then asked her if she had a last wish. 'Aye,' she said, 'dinnae strangle me; a'll burn as a am; an wuid ye untie ma airms an legs. An juist yae ither thing: can ye get ma twa pewter plates. A wuid tak them wi me.'

An officer went off to Maggie's lodging, found the pewter plates and returned. By this time, the crowd was agitated and cries of 'Burn the witch,' came from a few of the devout church-goers. In the main, the crowd was uneasy, fearing that it might be them next. The officer handed up the plates to Maggie, 'Thank ye kindly sir.' She looked to the executioner, 'Ye maun mak a low.' The man shoved a burning brand into the pyre and a second on the opposite side. As the smoke rose about her Maggie held the plates under her arms and began to flap them up and down. As she rose into the air, she called out jeeringly, 'Mind folks, it's mercat day the morra.' And with a mocking laugh she disappeared into the heavens.

To where Maggie flew, no one knows. Perhaps it was back to the Fincastle Mill to her beloved son, for it is said that the ghost of Broonie Clod still haunts it to this day calling, always calling, 'Me Masel! Me Masel!'

Maggie Mullach (sometimes Meg, Mag, Maug, May or Mieg and Moulack, Moloch, Vuluchd and even Hairy Meg) is often thought of as a brownie and even a banshee rather than a witch. She also had the capacity to reach down chimneys and steal children. There are, of course, many variations of Maggie Mullach tales. In some cases, Broonie is thought of as a Dobie, a dull-witted brownie, and guards the mill. Sometimes he is Maggie's husband or brother. Maggie is usually, and erroneously, accused of killing him. They are almost universally a tale with a moral.

43
Maggie Osborne the Witch

Claiming that she was the bastard child of Walter Whiteford, the Warlock Laird of Failford, Maggie Osborne set about making a name for herself as a spaewife or wise woman. Daughter of the laird she might have been, but whereas he had a wicked sense of humour, Maggie was just plain wicked. She did not have the patience to learn the country arts: to know the properties of plants that could do good. She preferred a greater understanding of herbs and fungi that would bend people to her will or just plain poison them. She also had an insight into human psychology but used it to manipulate people to her benefit. In time she conned and cheated enough people to afford the lease of a building on the Woodgate, in Ayr, where she set up a hostelry. The business ran well enough, but not well enough for Maggie: she wanted more and more.

The lack of satisfaction led her into darker ways. She set about collecting grimoires, manuals for evoking demons. Her argument was that you had to know your enemy; unfortunately for some, she was to become the enemy. In her basement, where she brewed ale, she created a secret room and set up an altar. After carefully reading the evocation texts, she conjured up demons to help in her nefarious deeds and from them she learned the art of flight and shapeshifting. In time she raised the Devil himself and became his acolyte. To ensure she remained undiscovered she carried out most of her devilish work in Galloway. Her normal route was over the Carrick Hills to Maybole, then south over the Nick of the Balloch, past a place still know as Maggie's Gate to Galloway. In Galloway she caused mayhem and disorder, stopping cows from producing milk, setting fire to haystacks, poisoning wells and drawing others, mainly women and young girls, into her sphere of influence. One time she attended a service at the Moor Kirk of Luce and there took the holy sacrament. Instead of swallowing the wafer she kept it in her mouth and as she left the church spat it out. It was there swallowed up by a toad who was in fact the Devil in disguise. The more she carried out Satan's work the greater powers he gave until she could even command the weather.

On one of her trips she saw a funeral procession come over the Nick and not wishing to be seen, changed herself into a beetle and hid in rut in the road. Unfortunately for her, and the perpetrator, she was stood on. Swearing vengeance, she discovered where the man and his family were living. Waiting until they were asleep in bed, she caused a heavy downfall of snow that caved in the roof of the house, killing all inside. The man had a son who, at the time of the crime, was away at sea. Not content with killing the man, his wife and seven children, Maggie also wanted the son dead. Knowing he was soon to arrive back in Ayr harbour she set about his demise.

'Richt lass,' she said to her maid, 'Pit some watter intae the mash-tun an float an ale-caup on it.' The girl did as she was asked. Maggie then went into her secret chamber and set about conjuring up the Devil to help her raise a storm. 'Whaur is the caup noo?' she called.

The girl looked in the mash-tun and saw the cup floating in the centre with ripples emanating from it. 'The middle,' the girl called back.

Maggie continued invoking her diabolical master. 'Whaur be it noo?'

The girl peered into the vessel again only to see the water raging and spilling over the rim, the cup was being violently inundated and capsizing. As she looked on in amazement, she could hear distant cries of fear and alarm. 'A dinnae like this Maggie it's no natural. A hear the cries o men droonin.'

'They'll cry lang ere a pity them,' said Maggie, 'Noo gang back an hae another luik.'

In a state of extreme agitation, the lass went back to the mash-tun and looked in, 'The caup is sankit,' she said.

'Then the Deil has servit me weel,' she said.

As Maggie carried out her unholy conjurations, a storm began to rage in the Bay of Ayr. An inward-bound vessel was caught in its throes and driven all ways by its ferocity. The captain and crew did their best to fight the waves, but to no avail. Relentlessly she was driven on to the Nicholas Rock and her timbers shattered. The crew and passengers were helpless in the tempestuous waters and all drowned, including the son of the man who had unwittingly stood on the malevolent Maggie.

In time, and inevitably, Maggie and her maid fell out. Realising that she was now in danger of exposure, Maggie set about the demise of the girl. 'A'm

gaun tae be a whiles busy lass but we need a pickle mair ale. Wuid ye stey back an dae a brew?' The girl agreed. That night as she was brewing, a clowder of cats entered the room. They began circling each other spitting and clawing. The girl moved out of the way to let them settle their apparent disagreements, but then one large and highly aggressive one broke away from the group and began to stalk the maid, pushing her towards the boiling liquid. It sprang at her throat almost causing her to stumble and fall in. However, the girl managed to sidestep and at the same time grab a ladle. She dipped it in the worts and threw the scalding fluid over the cats who fled. The stalking cat came at her again, but the lass quickly charged the ladle and threw it full in the feline's face. With a howl it ran from the room.

The following morning the maid, sure of what she would find, went to attend to her mistress. Maggie claimed illness and refused to come from beneath the covers, 'Naw lass a'm seek an cannae raise masel.' The girl took hold of the covers and hauled them from the bed. Maggie's face and shoulders were a mass of scald blisters.

'Ye are a witch Maggie an ye'll pey fer yer deeds.'

Maggie scowled and began to form a malicious cantrip, but the girl drew a Bible from her pinafore and held it up. Maggie withdrew back under the covers. With urgency the maid ran down the stairs and up to the provost's house to raise the alarm. The provost seconded some passers-by and together, Bibles in hand, they arrested Maggie. She was taken to the townhouse and locked in a small room beneath the stairs. She attempted many incantations, but a Prayer Book tied to the outside of the door ensured they were nullified. She did, however, manage to communicate with her master who offered her a way out of her intended fate. Faring extreme torture Maggie admitted her loyalty to the Lord of Hell and was spared the pain. Her trial was brief as she admitted her guilt to all the charges, including events she had no part of. The magistrate ordered that she be taken to the cross at the bottom of the Sandgate and burned to death.

On the day of her execution a large crowd had gathered to watch. She was dragged in chains to the cross and pushed on to the top of a pile of logs and peats. As they tried to tie her to the stake she pushed the executioner away. 'Ye'll no need tae dae that and ye dinnae need tae strangle me either. A'm no feart o the flames.'

'Weel, dae ye hae ony last requests afore we burn ye?' said the executioner.

'A hae lued ma pewter plates. There's twa o them on ma sideboard. Bring them tae me, but mak suir they dinnae get wat.'

A dragoon was sent up the Woodgate to Maggie's hostelry to collect the plates. He found them and made his way back down the stairs and into the street. His musket jammed a moment in the doorway causing him to drop a plate into a small puddle by the doorstep. He picked it up, shook the water off it and rubbed it dry on his breeches. At the cross he handed them up to Maggie.

'Thank ye kind sir; noo A'll juist awa.' She held the plates at the back of her shoulders and immediately they turned in to a great set of bat-like wings. 'A curse on ye aa. A'll be back tae bring mischief on ye afore lang.' She gave a hideous screeching laugh and as the wings began to flap, she rose in the air. Unfortunately for Maggie, the wing that had transformed from the plate dropped by the dragoon crumpled and the witch only rose some six feet in the air. A nimble dragoon leaped on to the logs and with his halberd, hooked Maggie and hauled her back down the earth. She was then bound tightly to the stake, had pitch poured over her and then set alight. Her screams of torment made even the hardest soldier wince. When all had cooled to ash, her remains were put in a sack and buried with a rough-cut crucifix at a secret location. And so Ayr's most famous, or is that infamous, witch went into history.

44

The Mermaid of Knockdolian

In Scottish folklore there are many water creatures: selkies, kelpies, uruisks, shellycoats, and of, course, the mermaid. In the time of Burns and Sir Walter Scott there were hundreds of such tales, now lost from the south of Scotland. Because of the continuing oral tradition in the Highlands and Islands and the work of local nineteenth century folklorists such as Alexander Carmichael, J. F. Campbell and J. G. Campbell, many of the northern Scottish tales still exist. Among the tales that still survive in the south-west is that of a mermaid. The story, in similar form, can be found on the Water of Urr in Galloway.

In Carrick is the hamlet of Ballantrae, *Baile an Traigh*, the settlement on the shore, long ago known as Kirkcudbright Innertig (though in truth that was a mile up the River Stinchar). In those times the landowning family was the Gordons. The young laird was the last of his line and owned Knockdolian, an estate that included the small mountain of the same name. His land was on the north side of the River Stinchar, a stream noted for its salmon, trout and an unusual denizen of the deep, a mermaid. Her wont was to swim up the river at high tide to a great black rock opposite Knockdolian Castle and sing to the world, but especially to the young laird whom she loved. She had often watched him in the fields toiling beside his workers. There was no job they did that he could not nor would not do himself. He, although nobody's fool, also treated them and their families with great respect and kindness. Because of this they gave of their best. The sea maiden understood that her love would never be consummated but sang on regardless. For his part the laird loved the mermaid for her songs and the way they lulled him to sleep at night. They gave him strange, wonderful dreams of far-off lands and exotic people, of warm oceans and soft breezes. That he could ever love her never occurred to him.

Being the last of his line, the young laird was keen to start a family and in time found a young woman with the right pedigree. It was not a love match and the young Gordon never expected it. He would do his duty to his ancestors and presumed that, in time, love would come. Was that not how things worked?

The marriage worked well enough, though he often found conversation at mealtimes a little strained. The young woman was also prone to sulking fits at any seeming slight. He found any kind of comment difficult and gradually bedtimes became almost impossible, so he slept in an adjoining room that had been his as a child. Regardless of this, in time they were blessed with the birth of a son. The laird was overjoyed and spent all possible time with the infant. His wife now seemed a little warmer and attended to the raising of the child herself rather than have a nanny.

The mermaid knew things had changed and grew jealous of this interloper who had come between her and the laird, so she increased her efforts. The laird in his turn still loved the mermaid's song and the sweet dreams they brought, but his wife grew more and more irritated and complained to her husband, 'Can you not do something about that devilish creature? Its wailing is keeping your son awake at night, not to mention me.'

He hadn't the heart to say that he loved the songs. 'It would be bad luck to try and stop her. I've just learned to live with it. Perhaps you can too.' She stomped off in exasperation.

A few weeks later the laird had to go to Edinburgh to attend to some legal matter and would be gone at least a week. He gave clear instructions to his workers, even arranging for an elderly retired couple to stay in the house to help his wife, if necessary. The following day the laird's wife called the foreman and two workers and instructed them to get sledgehammers and follow her. She strode earnestly to the river, the workers in tow. From the bank she pointed at the great black rock midstream, 'I want that stone smashed until there is not a single sign of it above the water.'

"But mistress, that is the mermaid's stane, an tae interficher wi that is suir tae bring misfortuin.'

She looked at the man, fury in her eyes, 'If you don't get rid of it, misfortune will befall you; for you and your family will be out of house and home. Do you understand me?'

"Aye mistress,' replied the man, a look of horror spreading on his face, as it did on his two colleagues. Sick at heart they waded into the river.

The lady heard the thud of the sledgehammers as they chipped away at the boulder. Two hours later the thuds ceased. With a smile of satisfaction, she suckled her child, before placing it in its cot in the nursery attached to her bedroom. She then went to her bed and waited for the arrival of the mermaid. She could not see it, but she certainly heard it: there was an unnerving scream that entered the very fabric of the building and shook it to its foundations. Though shaken herself, the laird's wife still found nerve to smirk at her victory. Then the voice came, it seemed to enter the room as a snake enters a burrow. The woman could hear it deep in her brain:

Ye may think on yer cot,
A'll think on ma stane,
But there'll ne'er be an heir
Tae Knockdolian again.

The woman scoffed and lay gloating at the defeat of her rival. It was a while before the siren's quatrain made sense, sending a shudder of apprehension through her. In dread she ran for the nursery. The scream's disturbance had somehow upended the cot and the child was smothered in his own bedclothes.

And so ended that line of the Gordon clan.

45

The Mermaid's Song

South of Culzean is Maidenhead Bay, named after the rocks that lie offshore. This stretch of sand has been used, time immemorial, as a point of arrival and departure by farmers and fishermen. One young fisherman, known only as William, kept his boat at the south end of the bay. After a day of fishing offshore he would sail back to the Maidens, haul the ketch up on the sand then sell his catch to the waiting crowd of farmers or their wives, farm labourers and the like. His pleasure was then to wander down towards the ruins of Turnberry Castle where he had a favourite spot to sit and watch the sun set over Arran. It was mid-June when the sun set late and rose early and the northern night sky remained in a glow and William, sitting on his usual perch, heard the siren song. At first it was distant and indistinct as if coming from every direction. As it swelled, he thought it came from of the sea between Carrick and Ailsa Craig. Pictures began to form in his mind of an everlasting land beneath the waves. A kaleidoscopic world of strange and alluring creatures, and merfolk of outstanding beauty who lived in coral-encrusted caves; the place of dreams where all was joy and happiness, a place where he would find an endless love. The song consumed him, and he knew he must go and find its source.

He half ran, half walked to his boat, pushed it into the waiting waves and rowed out past the breakers. He turned about, raised the sail and tacked his way west. The sky was clothed in soft, pink-edged summer clouds as the great golden ball of the sun fell towards the peaks of Arran. Westwards and further westwards he sailed and still the song was just out of reach, taunting and tantalising. The sky was now decked with pastel plumes of fire as the orb of the sun melted into Arran. Ailsey loomed larger and larger, then, as the first star appeared directly above, he passed its mighty form, his course set for the North Channel and beyond. Although a sailor of some experience he was now in unfamiliar seas, and worse, he paid no attention to the darkening sky ahead of him.

The wind began to rise causing him to take a deeper tack. Soon the spume was flying off the wavetops as he cut his way southwest, now northwest, the boat rising and crashing into the troughs. Still the mermaid's song possessed him and pulled him on and further on until he faced a massive lump of sea. It was only then he knew he had been glamourised. The mountain of water hit the ketch and effortlessly tossed it away. William's body arced through the air only to plunge into the brutal waves. For a moment he fought for his life. Then realising all was lost, he gave himself up to the sea and the siren's song.

46
Michael Scott

Michael Scot was a mathematician and astrologer and was revered as one of the great minds of the thirteenth century; so much so that he had the reputation of being a wizard. It was because of this reputation that it is said the Devil craved his soul. There are many tales regarding the challenges Scot set the Devil - sometimes just referred to as a spirit - so that he might not take his soul. In one the Devil is set three impossible tasks: one is to build a dam on the River Tweed at Kelso in one night, which he does; the second was to split Eildon Hill in the Borders into three, which he does. Lastly, and most famously, he sets the Devil the task of making a rope from sand. Here are a set of Ayrshire tales about Michael Scott one of which is another play on the same idea of the three challenges.

BIRTH OF MICHAEL SCOTT

A man from Dumbarton set sail aboard a ship bound for the East Indies. As they sailed south down the coast of Africa a storm erupted out of the north and threw the boat hither and thither until it crashed upon an isolated rock and the ship foundered. In the raging gale the crew perished beneath the turbulent waves. All that is, except the man from Dumbarton. Holding fast to a mast he was blown on to a deserted island. There was little in the way of food on this tropical rock, but there was a cave in which he was able to shelter from the fierceness of the sun; it also contained fresh water. A week later, as hunger cramped his belly, a mermaid swam into the cave. Both were equally surprised and pleased, he that he had company and a beautiful woman at that, albeit she had a tail. She was delighted, for recognising his predicament and on the lookout for a husband, she knew she had found her mate. Seeing that he needed food, she returned with a flagon of wine from a sunken ship and some fish. Unable to cook the fish he tore into the raw flesh, washing it down with the sour red wine. For many weeks they happily courted and cavorted in the sea. She was able to bring him fruits, fish and other food and, happily, the pool of fresh water filled during rainstorms. She also brought him gold, silver and jewels which she thought he might like. Having no use for them, he piled them up in the cave. For a year and a day, they shared a happy life and he almost lost his longing for human company. That was until one day a ship passed nearby and he automatically waved his arms and hailed it. A rowing boat was launched, and a group of sailors came and took him to the ship. He told of his isolation and captivity on the island, of his life with his mermaid wife and of the treasures she brought him. They offered to rescue him and his treasure, but the man loved his wife enough not to run out on her – for the moment anyway. He asked the captain if he might return in a year and a day, which he agreed to do. He also asked that the captain come in the early morning when his wife was away getting food. The captain also agreed.

True to the captain's word, a year and a day later the ship arrived, and the Dumbarton man boarded her with all his treasure, which he now had packed in sea chests collected by his wife from other sunken ships. The ship sailed northwards; Clyde bound. Later when the mermaid returned laden with food, she saw to her horror that her husband was gone and the cave emptied. With uncanny sense she followed in the wake of the vessel until she had caught up. She called out and demanded her husband be freed. The captain said he would do so only when she had untied a bag of hoops. The captain threw a large canvas bag of the hoops over the side. The mermaid opened the bag and drew out a hoop of rope. In the salt-water the rope became half impossible to untie. She tore at it with all her might, but unused to such tasks and with thin delicate fingers it took her a long time. By the time she had it undone, the ship was almost over the horizon and she still had a full bag to work on. By the time she had completed the task, the ship was back in the Clyde and the Dumbarton man was ashore at home. She hailed for him and asked that he return, but he refused, so she begged that in a year and a day he return one last time to their cave home for she had something vital to give him. He promised he would.

A year and a day later, true to his word, he caught a boat to his former home and went to the cave he had shared with his mermaid wife. She was waiting for him and in her arms was a child. 'Because he is part human,' she said, 'He cannot go to the sea and I dare not leave him alone for too long.' In tears she handed him their son. 'He can live on land and I ask, as he is your child also, that you take him and care for him and love him as I would, and you should.' The mermaid then pointed to a large case. 'There is another chest of jewels, which are his; that you must take. There is also this book, that only he can open, and only when he has wisdom enough.' Without another word, lest he see her grief, she dived into the sea and away.

The Dumbarton man returned to the Clyde but when the ship stopped off briefly at Ardrossan, he disembarked, for this was now his home. He called for a horse and trap which took him to his recently acquired home. In time the man died and his son inherited the building. A year and a day after his father's death, the son had enough wisdom to open the book; which he did. In it he found the means by which he could outwit the Devil and many glamouries, conjurings and spells that would make him the greatest sorcerer of his age. He was the Laird of Ardrossan Castle and his name, Michael Scott.

***

Using his mother's book, Michael gained the confidence to take on the Devil and use him to advantage. At this time Scotland was under a terrible taxation called the Pow Siller or head silver, a kind of poll tax on everyone, set by the Vatican in Rome. With a bad harvest and continuing trouble with England, Scotland was bankrupt, and the hardest burden was on the poor. Michael decided that he would go to Rome and encourage the Pope to halt the tax. The distance from Scotland to Rome is over twelve hundred miles and would normally take weeks to accomplish. Michael decided he would conjure up the Devil in the shape of a horse. Taking out his mother's book he found the right cantrip and raised Satan. The Devil snorted and protested but the spell held him in thrall. He led the horse to the top of the castle and leaped astride the great black beast, 'Munt Deil an flee,' called out Michel and with a furious whinny that shook the building to its foundations the horse kicked off into the sky, leaving a great hoofprint in the stone that is there to this day. High above the clouds they flew, thundering across the sky as if it was solid ground. Michael urged the Devil on, and the Great Deceiver wore down the miles. As they crossed the Alps his hooves shattered mountain tops. The beast seemed to enjoy the chaos this caused, so Michael hauled the reins and took them higher. 'Whit dae the auld wives o Scotland say when they gang

tae their beds?' asked the Devil through gasps of breath.

'Neer mind whit they say, juist flee.'

They sped on down the leg of Italy and soon reached Rome. Finding the Vatican from the air proved to be a simple task and in no time, they landed in St Peter's Square, much to the shock of the gathered pilgrims. As Michael and his mount advanced on the front door, the Swiss guards lowered their halberds to stop them. They may as well have presented blades of grass for all the effect it had; they were brushed aside. Inside, Michael respectfully asked that the Pope meet with him. He was told that under no circumstances would His Holiness see him. Fortunately for Michael, but more especially for the staff of the Vatican, the Holy Father was entering St Peter's Basilica and sought out the source of the commotion. 'What is all this?' he asked.

Michael looked down at the Pope, 'I have come on behalf of the people of Scotland to ask that you withdraw the tax on them as the country is under a great burden and the poor are suffering.'

'My son,' said the Pope, 'We are all under a great burden and no one suffered more than our Dear Lord.'

'Indeed, your Holiness, but he suffered that we might not, and by the look of the wealth that surrounds us here, the pittance that our people might give will make little difference; but it makes the difference of life or death to them.'

'It is a just command and cannot be overruled.'

'But you are the one who rules and made the rule in the first place therefore you can overrule it.'

'I have nothing more to say.'

'Well I have,' said Michael in a fury at the injustice. My steed here will make three stamps of his hoof and roar if you do not agree to our terms. The first will shake the Vatican, the second will bring down your chimney pots, the third will bring down the entire Vatican.' The Pope laughed in derision. 'This is the house of God.'

'If God wills it, it will stand,' said Michael, 'Should he will it otherwise, you will know his fury.'

Michael leaned forward and patted the neck of the now highly-strung horse, it stamped its front right hoof and roared: the building trembled. Clouds of dust fell from above. There were screams and howls of fear.

'Be not afraid,' shouted the Pope, 'It is merely an earth tremor, the Basilica has suffered many without harm.' He shot a look of contempt at Michael.

Michael remained calm and shook his head, 'You would not listen to reason nor the call for charity.' Well let me show you the power that is against you.' He leaned forward and again patted the horse's neck. It duly stamped its right hoof and roared, and a great physical tremor passed through the building. The was a sound of crashing and smashing as the massive chimney pots of the Vatican toppled to the ground.

'What say you Holy Father? Do you set my people free of this onerous tax and be remembered as a gracious and charitable Pope, or one who brought about the destruction of these sacred palaces?'

The Pope looked about at the pleading faces of his cardinals and priests. 'Very well, the tax is rescinded. I'll have my secretary draw up the papers.'

'Your grace has great wisdom and charity, and the faithful, if poverty stricken, people of Scotland will know and appreciate it.' The Pope merely gave a grunt.

Back in Scotland Michael delivered the Papal Bull to the royal palace at Holyrood and then took the skyway home.

Once at his own door he relieved the Devil of his glamourie, 'Wuid ye hae pattit ma neck a thrid time?'

Michael cocked his head, 'That's fer me tae ken an ye tae fin oot.'

'Hah! It wuid hae been a glorious sicht tae see that font o hypocrisy shatterit.'

'Hypocrites some o them micht be, but they keep ye in check ma Auld Clootie.'

'A dinnae like that name!'

'Guid,' said Michael, closing the door. He quickly opened it again, 'Whit dae auld women say when they gang tae their beds?'

The Devil laughed and looked at Michael who nodded his head, and in unison they said, 'That's fer me tae ken an ye tae fin oot.'

***

Auld Nick was keen to exact his revenge on Michael and perhaps gain his soul and thought long and hard on how he might achieve this. The idea came to him as he was having lie-down on his lava bed.

In an instant he was standing beside Michael in his laboratory. 'Ah, Auld Clootie, Hou are ye?

'I'm fine an a dinnae like that name.'

Whit wuid ye hae me caa ye?' asked Michael.

'Hou aboot, 'Yer Highness.'

'Naw! Naw!' said Michael. The only Highness A recognise is God hissel, an he cast ye doon.' He gave a wicked smile, 'Sae a sall caa ye Yer Lowness.'

The Devil looked at Michael in annoyance, 'Juist stick wae Auld Clootie.' Then a wicked grin passed briefly across his face. 'A hae a proposeetion fer ye.'

'Pray tell,' said Michael.

A'll warn ye first o aa: a am the Laird o Hell an a can dae onythin; bit if ye can think o onythin a cannae dae, a'll fill yer hat wi gowd.'

'Hoo mony goes dae a get?'

'Three.'

'An if a lose?'

'A get yer immortal saul.'

'Three impossible tasks ye say,' said Michael, unable to resist a challenge, 'Yer on.'

A look of glee crossed the Devil's face, 'Whit's yer first then, Auld… Auld…Snottie.'

'A like that wan,' said an unperturbed Michael, to the dismay of the Devil, 'Nou here's ma first impossible task. See that saun on the beach. A want ye tae mak a rope fer me ten yairds lang.'

'Nae bother,' said the Devil and strolled down to the beach to set about his task. A short while later he came back, 'Duin!' he said.

Michael offered him some wine and they chatted about this and that, then they both strolled down to the beach. 'Sae whaur is ma rope?' There was a look of horror on the Devil's face for the rope was nowhere to be seen. 'A tell ye whit, come an see me the morro an a'll gie ye anither chance. The Devil appeared next day again and set about his task. After a while he appeared beside Michael. 'This time.'

After another drink they walked to the beach and the rope was GONE! 'Dae a get anither chance?'

'Why no?' said a confident Michael.

As before the Devil appeared and set off to do his appointed task. He came back with a look of victory on his face. After wine and allowing for the tide to come and go, they went to the beach, and there before Michael's eyes was a magnificent rope. To say he was shocked would be an understatement. He swallowed hard at his possible fate. The Beast rubbed his scaly claws with pleasure. 'Neist task.'

Angry at his own stupidity, Michael could not think. He kicked at the rope, which held fast. On closer inspection he saw that it was shot through with another substance. On even closer inspection he saw it was bere caff. 'Haud on a meenit, Yer Lowness: ye hae cheatit. A wiz magnanimous an ye tuik advantage o ma kindness and cheatit. A suid hae expectit it. Ye mixed it wae another substance. A said saun, nuthin else, sae that's yin tae me.'

'Aye fine,' said the Devil, irritably, 'Whit's yer neist?'

'Richt, this time yer gettin nae second goes at it: furst time or nuthin.'

'A'm still gaun tae best ye, tak your immortal soul doon to Pandemonium and gently baste it on a bed o lava. What's yer,' Auld Nick gave a confident gloating chuckle, 'seicont impossible task?'

As Michael looked across the Firth of Clyde to Arran he noticed that the local stone that made up the coast was red sandstone. He knew that as a building material it was easy to quarry but not strong against the forces of the sea. All he needed to do was conjure up a powerful enough storm and any sea-based construction made from it would fall. 'Richt Lucy,'

The Devil's grin of satisfaction disappeared, 'Lucifer,' he said, through gritted teeth.

'I wis juist bein freenly an informal,' said Michael innocently.

'Get on wi it,' said the Beast.

'Whit a want is a brig biggit frae here at Hunterston across tae Great Cumbrae. Whit's that, aboot a mile and a hauf? That suid keep ye busy. An,' Michael paused for effect, 'Ye can only uise local stane an nae cement. Oh aye, an lastly, it maun owercome the first storm o the winter.' Now it was Michael's turn to smile with satisfaction.

'Ooh! Local stane ye say. Whit's the local stane?' it was now the Devil's turn to play innocent.

'I think ye'll fin it's saunstane.' The grin on Michael's face was so big it made his jaws ache.

'Saunstane? Mmm, with whunstane dykes,' said the Devil, a leer of pleasure spreading across his face

'Whunstane dykes?' said Michael, the grin instantly disappearing from his face; for Michael knew that whinstone could outlast granite.

'A'll juist awa and get on wi the job,' said the Auld Enemy gleefully and off he marched with a spring in his step. Soon he was at his task and in no time great piers of stone rose from the seabed. Michael could hear him singing some unholy anthem as he laboured away. Soon great arches of whinstone were set in place with great sculptured keystones of the Devil's own leering face embossed on it to add insult to injury. Firstly, he ran out the bridge from Hunterson then crossed over the Cumbrae to construct the other half. In no time at all each side was within a few feet of each other.

Michael's heart sank at the vision before him. At the same time, he was in awe of the craftsmanship of the Lord of Hell. The halls of Pandemonium must be a sight to behold, he thought. It would not only outlast the first storm of winter; it would outlast the worst. He shuddered at the thought of the eternal damnation he now faced as each of the last blocks slid into place. He was also half aware of a presence beside him. He turned to see a roughly dressed man with a bag of tools draped over his shoulder. The man looked at Michael and then to the bridge as the last stone was dropped in. 'A've been a mason these past thritty years, but truly, a hae neer seen the like.'

'Truly?' said Michael, hopelessly.

The man looked at him intently, 'I sweir bi Faither, Son and Haly Ghaist, I hae neer seen the like.' In that instant there was a great rumble and the bridge disappeared beneath the grey waters of the firth. Both men looked on open mouthed at the destruction and the Devil disappearing in an arc of fire.

'Aw, that's a shame, a disaster,' said the man.

'Indeed,' said Michael, resisting the temptation to run about in hysterical joy. 'I think that we should retire to that grand wee hostelry at Fairlie and allow me to purchase you a dram or two to lament this catastrophe.'

It was later that Michael chastised himself for such an obvious solution to his problem: the mere mention of the Lord was enough to topple the Devil's great handiwork. He was forever grateful to the old mason.

It was a week before the Devil appeared again. 'Lickin yer wounds wur ye?' said Michael.

'Dinnae be sae cocky. Ye hae bestit me twice, but ye still hae tae dae it a thrid time. Sae whit's it tae be.'

'The morra a want ye tae meet me up in Glenbuck at midday on the road tae Lanark an a'll tell ye whit it's tae be.'

That night Michael pulled out a kist and withdrew an old black velvet bonnet. He then cut a circular hole on the crown a fraction smaller than the gold coin he held in his hand. He then slipped a thin steel ring inside the bonnet that held it taut. One last look at his handiwork and he was ready. The following morning, he set up two mirrors and stood exactly midway between. He then recited an incantation and in an instant was in Glenbuck. He found his way to an exact spot he had found many years before and there he laid his bonnet carefully on the ground. Some twenty yards away was a large rock which he sat on and waited until midday. At the appointed time the Devil appeared. This time, for all the world, he looked like a handsome young man. 'Dressed tae kill, I see,' said Michael.

'Hopefully,' replied the Devil. He looked about the moorland. 'Guy dern place tae choose tae meet.'

'A like the solitude,' said Michael.

'Whit is it ye wish me tae dae?' enquired the Unholy One.

'I wish ye tae fill ma bonnet wi gowd coins.'

'But that is the prize a offert fer winnin the challenge.'

'But you didnae say it cuidnae also be the challenge.'

'Indeed, a didnae an a'm happy tae obleege.' The Devil smirked, 'What cuild be easier?' He shook his head, 'Ye gie yer life awa fer gowd. Juist lik maist humans.'

'Aye indeed, an a've een placed yin in the bonnet tae help.'

The Devil held out his hand and a stream of gold coins poured into the hat, dozens, then hundreds then thousands poured in a steady stream, yet the hat did not fill.

'Sorcery!' yelled the Devil. The challenge is void.' The stream of gold stopped abruptly

'I swear on ma life there is nae sorcery. Dinnae quit or a win.'

In exasperation the Devil continued the stream and on and on it flowed until Michael called out, 'Dae ye admit defeat?'

'Naw!' yelled the Devil, but Michael could see doubt in his eyes.

'Fine,' called back Michael, confidently 'Keep gaun.'

At last Michael could see the Devil's frustration was getting the better of him. 'Keep gaun,' shouted Michael knowing it would irritate.

'Eneuch,' shouted the Great Beast and the flow stopped.

'A win,' said Michael, 'an a claim ma prize. Ye maun noo fill ma bonnet wi gowd.' Michael thought Satan would burst with fury. His clothes burst into flames and the great Satanic form appeared. His eyes glowed volcanic bright and with a yell that echoed across the hills he shot off in a flash of fire and crashed through the Earth into the depths of Hell. Meanwhile Michael lifted his bonnet and the remaining coins in it fell through the hole he had cut and down into the airshaft of the ancient mineworkings below. He lit a twig of dead heather and dropped it into the hole. It fell a long way before landing on the tons of gold that lay in the deep mine. Eventually it would have filled, but the Devil wasn't to know that. Not only had he bested the Devil, but the Devil was now in his debt. A debt he would someday, somehow, have to pay back.

The remains of the Devil's Bridge or Deil's Dyke can still be seen to this day. It is in fact the igneous rock extrusions of Cumbraite that were formed when molten lava slid between the layers of sedimentary sandstone and formed the dykes sixty-five million years ago, give or take a week.

47 The Murder Hole

On the road that runs from Crosshill to Bargrennan by the Nick of the Balloch is the famous Rowantree Toll.

A young government officer was on his way from Wigtown to Ayr. His horse had gone lame at Wigtown and it was urgent that he report back to Ayr as soon as possible, so he decided to take to the road and walk the fifty miles. It would, he reckoned, take him a day and a half. With his official papers in a satchel on his back and his oilskin coat tied to it, he set out at a brisk walk. Unfortunately, he had been held up and didn't get away until just after midday and it was evening as he walked the track towards the Nick of the Balloch. To add to his misery a fresh wind was rising and brought a smirr that soaked his hair and face. The occasional cold trickle down his back made him curse that he had not thought to bring his broad-brimmed hat. In the coming darkness he could see a light that he presumed to be the Rowantree Toll Inn, a hostelry run by a widow and her two sons. He had stopped there briefly and had a great welcome. Perhaps he would take up their previous offer of a room, for the oncoming night had unnerved him, as the area had a reputation for people disappearing. Some said it was kelpies, others said it was bogles and some the Devil, looking for someone to boil in the kettles of Hell. As a man of the Enlightenment he did not believe in such superstitious trashtrie, but his old nursemaid's tales still worked their unchancy ways on the edges of his mind. He was quietly relieved when he arrived at the door, especially as the rain had thickened. He knocked and waited, but no one answered; he tried again but still no answer, so he went to the window and peered through a crack in the shutters. Although he couldn't quite make out what was happening, it looked like someone was pushing a pile of clothes into a trunk. He went back to the door and tried again. A second later the door was dragged open by a young man, the bottom scraping the beaten earth floor. 'Aw, it's yersel. Cam awa in. Sorry aboot that, we were juist preparin a gait fer supper.' He raised his arm to wipe his nose, a blooded long-bladed knife in his hand. The traveller entered in time to see the widow wipe up the last of the blood with a rag; her other son was sitting on the chest smiling. 'Dae ye wish a room fer the nicht?' she asked.

'Aye that wuid be grand,' he said.

'That'll be a shillin,' she said.

He automatically went to his pouch under his coat and wished he hadn't, noticing that all eyes were on it. 'I'll get it in a meenit efter a warm masel at yer ingle.' He stepped up to the fire, his back to the innkeepers, rubbed his hands then opened his coat and withdrew a shilling from his pouch, then let the heat wash over him. He closed the coat, turned and said, 'I think I'll hae a wee lie doon. A've cam a lang wey. Here's yer shillin.'

The widow opened a recessed door into a small single bedded room, handing him a lit candle on the way in. The sheets and blankets looked like they had seen a dozen previous guests, so he set the candle on the floor, pulled his coat about him, fell on to the bed and dropped off to sleep. A time later he was woken by a bang on the front door and voices. He presumed, correctly, it was another traveller on the road. He slipped back into a doze but was woken by the sound of a melee and a crash of chairs, a table upending and a thump just outside his room. The lad turned on his side and looked towards the door, then noticed blood seeping underneath it. He was out of bed in an instant. Outside the door he heard whispers, 'Whit aboot the boy in the bedroom. He must hae heard the stramash.'

'Aye, we'll dae awa wi him as weel an pit them baith in the hole.'

The lad turned and looked for an escape. The window was about a foot by a foot and near impossible. He could go through the door and rush them but with knives at the ready his chances were slim. First, he took the chair and jammed it under the latch, removed his coat and opened the shutter, he was met by a cold blast. He tried to squeeze through, but the window frame stopped him. He quietly dragged the bed over then kicked the frame with the heel of his right boot, again and again until it loosened. There was an attempt to open the door, so he re-doubled his efforts and franticly kicked. The bottom section gave, so he pulled at the rest with his hands, finding superhuman strength in his fear. Cut and bleeding, he hauled it away as the door began to give. He threw himself into the aperture and fell headfirst on to the rain sodden grass, losing a boot in the process. He headed in what he hoped was the right direction for the Nick. As he stumbled over bog and heather, he found the track uphill and began to run, behind him he could hear the sound of baying dogs. The hunt was on. As he ran, he continually stubbed his bootless foot or stood on large pebbles that bruised his instep. The sound of the hounds grew closer as he passed through the Nick and knew the dogs would get him before long. As he broke out the other side, he went off the track tripped over a boulder and free-fell into the cauldron of Rowantree Hill. He was airborne for a moment before somersaulting down onto scree that battered and bruised every part of him. Eventually he stopped in a soft mound of grass. Above him he heard the hounds stop and go silent, then voices, which eventually receded. Aching in every joint and muscle and bloodied, and now growing colder with the constant rain, he drew on a deep resolve for justice and staggered down into the Stinchar valley. He found his way to the farmstead at North Balloch and knocked on their door. He was given aid by the farmer and his wife, to whom he told his tale. It was decided that in the morning they should take the horse and cart and go to the Barr and raise a militia to apprehend the villains.

Later that day the citizen's army reached the inn, arrested the widow and her two sons and began a systematic search of the premises and surrounding area. In a room of the inn they found pouches, purses, items of clothing and other valuables that looked like the ill-gotten gains of crime. This was confirmed when one of the militia recognised a coat with a distinctive design that belonged to his neighbour who had inexplicably disappeared. The search of the surrounding area brought to light a sink hole from which emanated the odour of decaying flesh. A firebrand was thrown down to reveal at least four bodies. The head of the militia immediately created a court of law and after ten minutes deliberation it was decided to execute all three. Beams, spades and ropes were found, and three gibbets erected. The widow and her two sons were hanged and left to dangle in the wind for all to see. As there was a minister among the militia, a service was held at the Murder Hole, then the site was part-filled and marked by a large stone. The inn was then razed to the ground.

The young government officer was locally hailed a hero and a horse and trap supplied to take him on to Ayr. He was happy he had survived the ordeal and proud that he had ended a reign of terror. However, there were times when he was haunted by dark dreams and found himself falling endlessly into the Murder Hole.

The site of the Murder Hole was examined in 1818 by Alex Murray of Rowantree at the request of the Ayrshire-born folklorist Joseph Train. At that time the hole was found to be eighty feet deep.

As a Carrick family, we regularly cycled over the Nick of the Balloch and past Rowantree Toll. This story was often told or referred to when we stopped for a break at the top of the Nick.

In the Welsh annals there was a king of the northern British (Gwyr Y Gogledd) called Coel Hen which translates as Old Coel or Cole. In Ayrshire legend he was killed at the Battle of Coilsfield by an alliance of Picts and Scots under Fergus (see Dane Love's *Legendary Ayrshire*). The origins of the nursery rhyme are unknown and have been the subject of claims and speculation. The town of Colchester has tried to claim Old King Cole as its own, but the town was previously named Colnchester after the River Colne, so we can lay that claim to rest. The most likely explanation of the rhyme is that the name Coel Hen, who is also mentioned in the Welsh Annals and Arthurian literature, was famous enough to be translated as Old King Cole and that form of the name was used in a playful way by a rhymer. The rhyme itself is first attested to in 1708 though it seems to have been around in the oral tradition from a lot earlier. As Old King Cole (Coel Hen) has a definite historical link with Ayrshire, here is the Scottish version of the rhyme which appeared in the Herd Collection of 1776. There is a suggestion that sweet *Margarie* or Marjory is a refence to the mother of Robert the Bruce. That is not impossible.

Old King Coul

Old King Coul was a jolly old soul,
And a jolly old soul was he:
Old King Coul he had a brown bowl,
And they brought him in fiddlers three:
And every fiddler was a very good fiddler,
And a very good fiddler was he.
Fidel-didel, fidel-didel, went the fiddlers three:
And there's no lass in braid Scotland

Compared to our sweet Margarie

Old King Coul, etc.
And they brought him in pipers three:
And every piper, etc.
Ha-didel, ho-didel; ha-didel, ho-didel went the pipers;
Fidel-didel, fidel-didel, went the fiddlers three.
And there's no lass, etc.

Old King Coul, etc.
And they brought him in harpers three
Twingle-twangle, twingle-twangle, went the harpers;
Ha-didel, ho-didel; ha-didel, ho-didel went the pipers;
Fidel-didel, fidel-didel, went the fiddlers three.
And there's no lass, etc.

Old King Coul, etc.
And they brought him in trumpeters three:
Twara-rang, twara-rang, went the trumpeters three;
Twingle-twangle, twingle-twangle, went the harpers;
Ha-didel, ho-didel; ha-didel, ho-didel went the pipers;
Fidel-didel, fidel-didel, went the fiddlers three.
And there's no lass, etc.

Old King Coul, etc.
Ant they brought him in drummers three:
Rub-a-dub, rub-a-dub went the drummers;
Twara-rang, twara-rang, went the trumpeters three;
Twingle-twangle, twingle-twangle, went the harpers;
Ha-didel, ho-didel; ha-didel, ho-didel went the pipers;
Fidel-didel, fidel-didel, went the fiddlers three.
And there's no lass, etc.

49

The Selkie

The following tale is common to the Atlantic fringe of Scotland but has its origins in Shetland folklore and earlier into Norse - versions of it are found in Norway and Iceland, recorded by Icelandic folklorist, Jon Arnason, in the mid nineteenth century and called Selshamurrin, Seal Skin. Jon Gudmundsson, a self-taught academic, recorded a very similar tale in Iceland in 1641. A plausible explanation for the idea is Norse contact with the Inuit in their sealskin boats and clothes. When removing their clothes to dry after fishing in their kayaks they might give the impression of shapeshifting from seal to human form.

John MacWalter was a young fisherman who lived on the Ayrshire coast. He was a contented young man in love with his work and in no hurry to marry. He was handsome, successful and, when in town, an attraction for the young women. But John took no interest in them; his first love was the moving ocean and its moods and eccentricities; it filled his deep heart with poetic longing. He would happily row for hours to lay creels for crabs and lobsters and nets for cod and herring. Other times he would drag a long-line strung with hooks to gather up shoals of tiger-striped mackerel. On summer evenings he loved nothing more than to raise the sail and, with a gentle south-westerly breeze, glide home over the soft waves while watching the sky over Arran turn incandescent.

His other love was the still hours of dawn when the growing light defined the contours of the land and turned the sea to palest blue. It was one such morning as he walked out that he saw shadows move on the beach. In silhouette they were obviously human, yet no-one around in this Presbyterian world ever perpetrated such acts, for these people danced with joy and abandon. They swayed like kelp in the waves. In their revels they pranced, promenaded, twisted and turned with supreme elegance. Jon was enthralled. He realised these were the selkie, the people of the sea: shapeshifters in two worlds. As he moved closer, he spied a lone figure walking along the sand, as if caught up in a reverie. She was tall and lithe and moved with perfect grace. He couldn't draw his gaze away from her. He felt a deep surge of emotion he had never known, one of love and desire. He needed her, he wanted her and when he saw her skin laid upon the rocks, he thought to capture her for his own. Removing his boots, he crept on stocking soles up to the rocks, slid the skin off and walked boldly away. In an instant that metaphysical connection between the selkie and her skin was put under stress and she spun about and ran towards the thief. John ran for home grabbing his boots on the way. Behind the woman, a man broke away from the dancers and followed her, but on reaching the boundaries of the shore he stopped and watched as she pursued her vital skin.

At his cottage John hurried inside and quickly folded the pelt on his table, he then removed a loose stone under the eaves, slid the hide in and replaced the stone. He walked back to the door and opened it. The woman stood there, unashamedly naked, 'Please return my skin so that I may return to my home.'

'No!' he said, a hard, unsympathetic edge to his voice. 'You are the most exquisite creature I have ever seen, and I wish you for my wife.'

'Have you no heart, man of the land?'

'Yes, and it is entirely yours. In time you will come to love me too.'

Hardening his heart against her pleas, John bid her wait while he went into town to buy clothes for her. His choices, though plain, were of good taste and his eye for size ensured they fitted well. The woman, who said to call her Mara, was hardly able to do less and resigned herself to her fate. First thing she did was to set about learning the ways of the people of the land. Within a year she had a child, then twins then four more besides – three girls and four boys. She did indeed grow to love John and adored the children she had by him and was the perfect mother, as John was a father, teaching the children the songs and lore of her people. She swam with them in the firth, ran along the beaches gathering shellfish and seaweed. She did not know the people of the land's names for them, so she gave them selkie names and they ate them raw. As they grew, John would take them out fishing with him, so even at the age of six, the eldest child, a girl, could charge the creels, feed out the nets and longline as well as many and better than some. At times the selkie lass would hear her people calling from the sea and would wander down and listen to them. One voice filled her with deep sadness and longing, so she would turn away and go back to the house. Other times she would take the children and listen to the songs of the sea. The children instinctively understood and called back so that heads would pop up all along the beach causing wonder and intrigue on both sides.

One fateful day, the three boys and the eldest girl were out with their father fishing, a boy and a girl were helping on a local farm and the youngest, a four-year-old was with her mother. The child was sitting in a creel humming a selkie tune while her mother prepared fish on the table. 'Darling child,' she said, 'that is so beautiful. When I was a selkie I used to take off my skin, sit among the rocks and sing that very tune.'

'You took off your skin?'

'Yes, it was of silver-grey fur and I could wrap it about me and swim deep in the ocean with my good man.'

'You mean a coat like Daddy looks at sometimes.'

Mara's head spun round, 'What coat is that, dearest?'

'The one he keeps up there,' said the girl pointing to the eaves.

The seal woman went straight to where her child had pointed and felt until she dislodged the stone. Taking down her precious pelt. She went to her child, kissed her sweetly, and ran from the house. As she raced to the water, she drew the skin about her and dived into the welcoming sea. The exhilaration and joy were almost overwhelming. She glided along the waves' edges, dived deep then torpedoed her way to the surface clearing the water by many feet, twisting and falling backwards into the waiting ocean. Now she was on a mission, a search, and swam out into the depths of the firth. Towards her came a boat with a man and four children rowing towards the shore. She looked up and saw the face of her fisherman husband, she saw his recognition, his horror, his despair. 'Oh man of the land, I loved you; but more I loved my man of the sea.' She sank beneath the waves, her heart touched with sorrow but her soul longing for her lost, true love.

Some say she left and never returned, others say she returned sometimes and sang to her children or danced with them at daybreak. One tale suggests that all the children, but one, finally returned with her to the sea. The boy who remained loved the land too much to leave it and became a farmer. But who could not wish them well?

50

The Serving Maid and the Devil

In 1682 Major-General Robert Montgomerie of Irvine and his new, young wife had, for weeks, been preparing Seagate Castle for a visit by the Earl and Countess of Eglinton. A man still on the rise, considering his age, he was keen to make a great impression on their aristocratic kin and neighbours. The house was swept and dusted top to toe, windows sparkled, every piece of brass polished, every wood surface shone like a mirror, especially the dining table. The best tableware was hired, and their own silver unlocked and made ready. The general made one last inspection, and all seemed to his satisfaction, until he walked round the table and noticed that some small, but valuable, items of silverware were missing. He called his steward who said that he had inspected the table earlier and all was present. Someone had removed them for further cleaning, or they had been stolen. A quick interview of the staff showed that the latter was the case. As all the staff except one had been with the Montgomeries for a considerable time, the exception, a girl from Ireland called Dearbhla, was the obvious suspect. The steward grabbed her by the arm and roughly hauled her into the presence of Montgomerie and his wife.

'What have you done with our silver, girl?' said the General, sternly.

'This is an injustice. Because I am new, or perhaps because I am Irish, you presume that I would commit an act of thievery. I was raised a good Christian and a respecter of the Commandments. Besides, I have never been in the dinner room, as it was out-of-bounds to me. So, there is no chance I would have laid even a finger on whatever has gone amissing.'

The girl was so impressive in her defence that the general said he had perhaps been a little too quick to judge.

'There is no doubt, your lordship…' said the girl.

'General will do,' he interjected.

There is no doubt your General Lordship, that the culprit still skulks within these walls and even if I have to raise the Devil mesel, I will find the one that did it.'

Sir Robert dismissed the girl, though her ungodly rant unsettled him a little. He let it go as Irish temper. He and his wife then settled down to discussing how they might take it further with the rest of the staff.

Meanwhile, the girl, true to her word set about raising the Devil. She went out into the yard and collected tail feathers from the black cockerel, then she then went to the gardener's shed and borrowed a riddle. With these and a copy of the Bible she went down into the cellars of the house. Knowing she would only be allowed three questions she went over them muttering the words to ensure they were exact. She then scored a circle in the floor. Stepping inside she rolled the riddle round the scoring with her left hand in an anti-clockwise direction while holding the feathers and the bible in her right hand. This done, she read Psalm 51 for protection:

> Have mercy on me, O God,
> according to your unfailing love;
> according to your great compassion
> blot out my transgressions.
> Wash away all my iniquity
> and cleanse me from my sin.

She then read the first verse from Chapter 13 of the Book of Revelation:

> And I stood upon the sand of the sea, and saw a beast rise up out of the sea, having seven heads and ten horns, and upon his horns ten crowns, and upon his heads the name of blasphemy.

Outside, thunder rolled over the house and the general's wife cowered in terror under the bedclothes. Though safe within the circle, Dearbhla watched in trepidation as the Devil rose out of the ground, strangely attired in a seaman's outfit. 'What do you wish of me?' he said in a strange sweet and friendly voice.

'Do you know of the missing silver within this house?'

'Yes.'

Dearbhla then threw three of the feathers at him, 'Return to where you came from.' He sank back into the floor. She then read the verse from Revelation backwards. The Devil fully rose again, this time dressed in a Harlequin outfit. Standing on one leg, his right foot against his left thigh, he said, 'What do you wish of me?'

'Where is the missing silver within this house?'

'Under the bed off the thief,' he said, a hard edge to his voice.

The girl threw three more feathers, 'Return where you came from.' The devil once more vanished into the ground. One last time she read the verse from Revelation backwards. This time the Lord of Hell rose from the ground like some grotesque, hirsute, clawed reptile. His tail whipping sideways sending a case of empty wine bottles crashing into the wall. All over town the dogs began howling. 'What do you wish of me?' His voice was a menacing rasp. Dearbhla could hardly get the words out for fear and trembling, 'Who stole the silver?'

'James Berwick.'

The girl threw the remaining three feathers and with a deafening clap of thunder that shook the building, the earth swallowed up the beast. In his wake remained the pungent smell of brimstone.

Dearbhla found her way to Montgomerie's study and knocked on the door. 'Enter,' came a less-than-imperious voice. When she opened the door, the general stood at the fireplace a wary look on his face.

She curtsied and said, 'The silver is under the bed of James Berwick. He is the thief.' With the girl in tow the old soldier marched down and straight into the bedroom of his steward. The man was sitting in bed reading the Bible, a look of fear on his face. The general knelt and peered under the bed; his arm went in and pulled out a wooden box. Opening it, he unwrapped a cloth and found his missing silver. He unceremoniously pulled the man from his bed, removed the Bible from his hand, 'You should have paid attention to that before: Exodus 20; 2-17, the Ten Commandments, number eight.' He opened the front door and threw the man into the street. 'Thou shalt not steal,' he said, and slammed the door. He turned to the girl, 'As for you, young miss, pack your bags and I will decide your fate in the morning. A bewildered lass went to her room and packed. In the morning she was asked to wait in the pantry. The General called for the local cleric who escorted her to the tolbooth for trial accused of witchcraft.

Two days later she was tried by the local judiciary including the town provost. 'Have you anything to say for yourself before we pass sentence, 'Yes Your Majesty.'

'Provost,' interjected the official.

'Yes, your Provost Majesty. I was in possession of the Holy Book at all times and read from it. It was a trick showed to me in Ireland by a Doctor Colvin.'

'In that case, you admit your guilt and we sentence you to two years in the tolbooth.'

The poor girl was dragged away and placed in confinement. She was imprisoned in chains behind three stout doors. When the officer of the tolbooth checked in the morning the Irish girl was gone. She was never seen again, and her fate is unknown. That was another trick Doctor Colvin showed her.

51

Sithichean nan Leargaidh Ghallda

THE FAIRY FOLK OF LARGS

In the long ago past when Largs was just a village the place was inhabited by the fairy folk

Local people called the village, the *Lairgs*, which is more in keeping with its Gaelic name of An Leargaidh Ghallda – *the Lowland Slopes*. In those long-ago times, the clachan was the home of the *sith* (pronounced shee), the fairy folk. Their usual haunt was Knock Hill (literally hill hill) and the old Tron (weighing) Tree in the centre of the village. The tree was later cut down and the pig of the man who felled it was found dead the next morning. Presumably cursed by the fairies.

A hawker was on his way to Largs to sell his wares. As he approached the Noddle Burn, he met with a woman of the fairies. She pointed into his basket and said, 'Would you be kind enough to give me that bowl?'

'Aye,' he said, 'That'll be a bawbee.'

'I need a bowl, but I never use money.'

'Nae money, nae bowl.'

'I can reward you in other ways by bringing you good luck.'

'A mak ma ain luck. Noo, if ye dinnae mind, I'll be aff.'

'As you please,' said the woman.

The man continued down the hill to the Noddle Water and Largs but due to the previous night's rain the track was wet and on one particularly steep part he slipped and sent his basket flying over his head. The entire contents, including the crockery, careered down the slope. In trepidation he began to gather it up and happily found that all the plates and bowls were still intact. That is, all except one: the very bowl the fairy woman had desired. It was smashed beyond repair so he discarded it. However, later in the day he found a silver knife that made up for his loss. Had he known the woman was of the sith, he would have realised that an act of kindness would have been better rewarded, as it always is.

On market days in the village the sith would quietly steal pieces of wool that was set out for sale to use in making their clothes. But they never took anything without making up in some other way. Were you to provide them with shoes and stockings you could be guaranteed good luck forever.

Away with the fairies is a common expression for someone who is not quite of this world. Long ago it was common belief that if the fairies took you, a night could last as long as seven years. So it was with a gentleman of Largs who went off with them to Haylie Toll where he danced all night long. Although he came back many years later, as far as he was concerned it was a single night. He had a wonderful time but the only thing that had disconcerted him was that one of the dancers had no head.

Fairy children were kept scrupulously clean, but the sith preferred water from a bucket rather than the stream, so it was their practise to enter houses at night for that purpose. If no water was available, then they washed their children in the 'kit' or sowens water, which was always available. One night, in a weaver's house, after such an escapade, the sith left a hat behind. They removed it the following night.

(Sowens was made by steeping oat husks in water for a week where it ferments. The liquid is sieved off and put in a bowl where it separates into a slightly alcoholic liquid and an oaty mass. The liquid (sowens water) is put in a jug for drinking and the oaty mass can be eaten with salt raw or cooked.)

Another time, a couple were fast asleep but were awakened by someone on their bed. When they looked up in the dim light of the peat fire, they saw two fairy women pass by laughing, walking and talking. They disappeared and a moment later two fairy men made the same trip, wondering to each other if the fairy women were behind them.

A man on his way down out of Largs passed by a fairy dwelling where he cut a branch from an ash tree to use as a walking stick. On his return later that evening as he passed the fairies his stick caught on a stone, tripped him and sent him flying down the hill. As he picked himself up, he was taunted by gales of laughter. Later that night he was hoisted out of his bed and taken away to a place he could not remember. He woke in the morning in his byre sitting astride his cow while holding its horns for balance.

(The above tales were told to folklore collector, Rev. J. G. Campbell, by an unnamed servant girl while on a visit to Largs.)

The year was 1867 when a coach was seen proceeding through Largs towards the burying ground. This was not unusual for the time, but as there was no sound of hooves or the rumble of the coach's wheels, local people took it as a bad omen. Shortly afterwards a wealthy lady of the town died, 'not in the odour of sanctity'. Some thought she was in league with the devil and it had been a sign of Satan calling her home. She was locally known as Brimstone Betty.

(Not in the odour of sanctity, i.e. the smell of brimstone or sulphur, which is associated with the Devil)

There were certain people in Largs in the nineteenth century, said to be three in number, that it was deemed unlucky to meet. Should a fisherman be so unlucky as to pass one of these people, he would turn about and go home.

52
The Stirk in the Kirk

A young black Galloway stirk or bullock was loose and grazing in the grounds of Kirk Alloway. As it cropped the grass around the narrow doorway, one horn entered the kirk. Spying large clumps of grass inside the building, the beast turned its head and performed the seemingly impossible act of getting both horns and head inside. It continued to graze happily for an hour then, having eaten the supply, it sought to leave. Each time it advanced on the door its horns hit the door jambs. Realizing this was fruitless, it went around the windows, but each was too high and too narrow. It tried the door again without success. Having exhausted all the possibilities, it lay down for the night. Next day it tried again and again but only served to give itself a headache. Frustrated on all points, it began to bellow, and some local people attempted to release it, only to have the beast attack them. By day three the stirk was wild with hunger and had bellowed itself hoarse. The sound that came out was almost a shriek.

As twilight fell on that day, two twelve-year-old girls made their way home. Just short of Kirk Alloway they began discussing its supernatural history, 'It's haunted by the Devil,' said one.

'There's nae sic a thing. It's juist supersteetion,' said the other.

'Aiblins, but it's still a wee bit scarey.'

'Naw its nooooo...'

The voice trailed off a as a great black horned head rose up at the window and gave a great bellowing shriek. Some say that the double track they left behind was the origin of the A77.

53

Sunday Roast

Crossraguel Abbey was the centre of learning for Carrick in the late medieval period. Not only was it rich in knowledge, it was also rich in terms of worldly wealth; with high-yield farmland, good sheep pasture and thick seams of coal on nearby Craigfinn. But times were changing, and the old Catholic order was being swept away and replaced by Protestant Presbyterianism. Now the former bishop's seat was being placed *in Commendam*, which is to say, in trust, and the post of commendator, to run the trust, was created. Such a post always brought wealth and power.

Gilbert Kennedy, fourth Earl of Cassillis was a man on the make and saw the position of commendator as another rise in his grab for glory. As far as he was concerned, he was the rightful person for the job as his uncle Quinton Kennedy had been the last abbot. Unfortunately for him, others saw it differently, perhaps wary of the earl's quest for power, and appointed Alexander Stewart of Kilwinning to the post. Kennedy was incensed and swore retribution. He would have the commendator's job, Hell or high water. He was not known as the King of Carrick for nothing, and there was no room for two.

Alexander Stewart was a shrewd man who had courted those in positions of power and risen in influence as a result. He had also committed the unforgivable sin of developing a friendship with another Kennedy, the Laird of Bargany: a power-rival to Cassillis. When Stewart first went to look over Crossraguel and its lands, he stayed with Bargany – a red rag to the bull that was Gilbert Kennedy. While he strode about his castle fuming, a plan began to form in his mind. It was after he had remarked that Stewart could burn in Hell. 'Never mind Hell, 'he thought, 'He'll burn here.'

With his plot fully formed, he ordered his retainers to set out and locate the usurper. It didn't take long as Stewart travelled in style and was quite conspicuous; he was located in new woodland near the abbey. As he strolled through trees with two servants he was confronted by a band of fully armed riders. One look in their faces and he knew he was in trouble.

The grim earl looked down on his prey, 'Welcome tae Kennedy country Mr Stewart. A pleisant land, dae ye no think?'

'Indeed, it is Mr Kennedy.'

'Ma Lord.'

'I'm sairry,' said Stewart, not understanding the response.

'Ye will caa me, ma lord.'

'As ye wish.'

'A wish.' It was said with a growl.

'Whit can a dae fer ye,' Stewart paused, 'ma lord?'

'A was thinkin o showin ye roun this pleisant land o oors.'

'Yer kinsman has aaready duin that, thank ye.'

'Aye, Bargany; but he bides by the Girvan Water. A was thinkin, aiblins a wee visit tae the seaside. They say it is guid fer yer health.'

'A'm no shuir a visit wuid be aa that guid fer mine, ma lord.'

'Aye, weel ye are aboot tae fin oot.' Kennedy turned his horse about to face his men, 'Tak him!' he commanded.

At Dunure, Stewart was unceremoniously shoved into a small locked room to await his fate. The following day he was dragged into the kitchen. 'Mr Stewart, it is near dinner an we are a wee bit short on meat sae we decided that roastit commendator suid be on the menu.'

Stewart looked at the red-hot coals in horror

'Afore we consign ye tae the fire, a wuid ask ye tae sign these documents haunin ower the richts tae the lands o Crossraguel, which are richtfully mine.'

'A cannae dae that, ma lord. The lands belang tae the kirk an no tae me. A am but the commendator, no the awner.'

Kennedy paused for a moment, but in his mind he thought that in these troubled times, while the church was in flux, all he needed was a document stating his ownership and that would secure the lands for him. 'Sign the document or roast.'

The commendator looked into the implacable eyes of the earl, 'A cannae.' His fate was sealed.

'Strip him an get him on the spit. Mak shuir you lard him weel sae he'll broon up nicely,'

The poor man was roughly stripped naked, his arms pulled behind and tied at the elbow. He was then callously bound to the spit then lifted on to the cradle. As he hung suspended above the searing heat, the cook began to pour molten fat over him which dripped and ignited on the fire sending up scorching fingers of flame. The commendator could resist no more and screamed, 'Get me aff, a'll sign it.' The kitchen staff lifted him down and released the rope. 'Watter, please wash me in cauld watter, a beg.' Cassillis lifted a bucket of water and drenched the naked man. When dried and clothed he was taken to the table with the manuscript and duly signed. Alexander Stewart was then imprisoned in Dunure until his wounds healed. The earl assumed no one would believe such a fantastic tale should Stewart decide to inform on him.

What seemed like a brilliant ruse turned out to be nothing of the sort, as Kennedy later found out that the document was not legal unless witnessed and signed by an official notary. A new document was scribed, a bribable notary found and the earl returned to Dunure, 'Ye need tae sign this new document in front o this gentleman,' said Cassillis.

Time, they say, is a great healer, and Alexander Stewart had repaired not just in body, but also in mind. He resolutely refused to sign. Once more the flames licked about his naked body causing him to scream. His anguish was ignored as the earl said, 'Stuff an aiple in the grise's mou.' As no apple was to hand, the cook shoved his napkin roughly into Stewart's gaping mouth, stifling another scream.

'Will ye sign?' roared the earl.

The commendator nodded furiously. The rag was removed, 'A'll sign, a'll sign.' He remained conscious long enough to scribe his name on the document before fainting. The notary and the early signed below.

To keep witnesses silent cost Gilbert Kennedy a considerable sum. He did, however, miss a young kitchen porter who found he had no incentive to keep his mouth shut. Soon after, word got to the Laird of Bargany who sent his men to Dunure to rescue the unfortunate man. Bargany's men entered the castle with ease as there was only a basic staff there. They were in the process of freeing Stewart when Gilbert Kennedy arrived in force with his own men and besieged the castle. The Bargany men held them off with comparative ease using harquebus guns and stones from the walls. They also threatened to dismantle the castle if Cassillis did not withdraw. His mind was made up quickly when a strong force of Bargany reinforcements arrived promising to avenge the wronged commendator.

Alexander Stewart was taken to Bargany where he lived out the rest of his days, a severely damaged man. The Earl of Cassillis was hauled before the Privy Council then the King and his Council and ordered to pay two thousand pounds. By the law of the time he should have been brought up before the Court of Justiciary, but Kennedy was a King's man and needed in the political struggles of the time, so *Real Politic* played its part and Gilbert Kennedy, apart from the fine, remained unpunished. Even the Laird of Bargany did not follow through on his promise of revenge. There were greater forces at work, and now was not the time to make more enemies.

But did the commendator finally receive his justice? The same story is told of Gilbert Kennedy as was later told of his kinsman Archibald Kennedy, that when he died a boat in the Firth of Clyde was asked by a passing ship as to where he was bound, the reply was, 'From Hell to Cassillis for the soul of Gilbert Kennedy.' On the way to his funeral a crow landed on the carriage and the horses halted and would not move until the crow flew off. This happened three times convincing everyone that the Devil had come to claim his soul.

54

Tae see oorsels as ithers see us

Back in the days when people were either self-sufficient or dead, a shepherd would head off into the remote highlands south of Barr with nothing more than some ham and scones rowed up (tied up) in his plaidie, which also served as his bed and blanket. One such worthy, having run out of food, ventured to a cottage and asked if he might borrow a mirror. The gudewife produced one, enquiring why he needed it. 'A juist wantit tae see whit a man luikit like deein o hunger in his ain land.'

The gudewife lifted her besom (brush) and chased him off the croft. 'Twis worth a try; but weel she kent me fae afore,' he said with a laugh.

55

Tam Giffen

Aul grannie sat cardin her woo by the fire, — *brushing*
On a caul winter eve; an, as midnicht drew nigher, — *nearer*
The bairns gathered roun her an quitted their glee
To list to a tale: mony aul tales had she, — *listen, many*
O broonies, an spunkies, an wee merry men — *house elf, will of the wis*
That dance in green jackets aa nicht in the glen;
O ghosts an wild spectres in aul castles grey,
That haud their wild revelries till break o day.

In a circle aroun her the wee bairnies drew,
An eerie they leuked at the fire burnin blue; — *fearful, looked*
Nae whisperin was heard when aul grannie began
Tae tell o Tam Giffen, the wild warlock man. — *male witch*
Lang, lang in the warld, won'd warlock Tam; — *world, lived*
Nae ane could tell frae whi kintrae he cam; — *country*
He seemed like a stranger on earth left forlorn,
An some said he ne'er in the world was born.

He wandered the kintra, east, north, south and west,
An gaed aye to ca on them wha used him the best; — *always, call*
Alane in some glen he at morn micht be seen,
But nae ane kent whaur he micht be or twas een. — *knew, in the evening*
Pale, pale was his lank cheek, but dark loured his brow, — *frowned*
An his black ee seemed glancing wi' unearthly low, — *flame*
He lauched at the sorrows that made ithers weep, — *laughed*
An never was kent to slumber or sleep.

In through the keyhole, or doon through the lum,
When doors were aa barred, he at midnicht wuid come;
Or afar in some glen wi the bogles wuid be, *goblins*
Aa the deid o the nicht, haudin unhaly glee; *holding*
Or dancin wi fairies far ben in the wud, *inside, wood*
Or sailin on cockleshells far oer the flud, *flood*
Or fleein wi' witches awa through the air,
Or daein dark deeds that a daurna declare. *dare not*

Wi a sly noiseless step ben the house he wuid come,
An set himself doon by the side o the lum,
An mutter dark words wi a straunge eldritch soun, *unearthly*
An luik as if somethin was steerie around, *disturbing*
Whilk naebody cuid see but himself;
An then tae the folks he would strange stories tell
O witches and spectres, and grim goblins near,
That, flittin in corners, to him did appear. *shifting*

When a tempest was brewin afar in the sky,
There aye was a wildness in Tam Giffen's eye;
An awa oot o' sicht he wuid soon disappear,
Crying, 'wark's to be dune an' I daurna bide here'; *work*
An aft, wuid gude folk in terror declare, *often*
He rade in the black storm on high in the air, *rode*
Leadin whirlwinds onward o'er valley and hill,
Working mischief an ruin tae guid an tae ill.

When Tam saw a priest he grew wild as a stirk, *young bull*
An never wad enter the door o the kirk;
If ony ane near him attempted to pray,
In a moment Tam Giffen wad vanish away;
If ony by chance ever mentioned his name,
Suin, suin to their terror an wonder he came,
An' speir'd whit they wantit by caain him there, *asked, calling*
When he had got business tae dae in the air.

Ae nicht when a revel o goblins had been, *party*
Faur doon in the glen on the muin-lichtit green, *far*
Tam shared in the glee, an next morning telt aa
The wonderful things that he heard an he saw;
Then the fairies an goblins an witches did meet
By Garrit's deep linn – a wild lonely retreat,
An wailins were heard in the dreid midnicht air, *dreaded*
An Tam Giffen, next mornin, was found lifeless there.

J. D. Brown c. 1845

Walter Whiteford, otherwise known as the Laird of Fail, was a kenspeckle figure whom many assumed to be a warlock: they were quite correct, of course. Well, to be precise, he was more of an alchemist and had studied on the Continent under some of the great masters. He could speak many languages and dressed in the Continental style which, to local people, gave him an eccentric appearance. It was said he conjured up demons to assist him in unholy rites and rumour was that even the Devil had visited Fail Castle. The Laird certainly had learned to command the elements and produce weird effects through strange alchemy.

He was out hunting with his friend, Sir Thomas Wallace of Craigie, when the they caught the smell of brewing on the wind. The laird's keen nose took them to a butt and ben where a woman was busy making beer. Sir Thomas knocked on the open door and the woman, recognising gentry, invited him in. Right behind him was Walter. The woman took one look at dandified Whiteford, screamed and pushed him back through the door, 'It wis him that causit ma coo an ma dug tae dee an ma wean tae gang gyte, no tae mention coupin ma kirn.' She looked at Craigie, 'I'll gie a pint stowp tae yer lordship, but that deil will get naethin.'

'Hae yer drink Tam, I'll wait oot here by the naigs,' said the laird. He closed the door, removed a pin from his lapel and jammed it into the top of the door frame. The woman poured out the beer from a bucket into the stowp and handed it to Sir Thomas. She had no sooner done so than her foot began to move around of its own accord. Wallace peered at her as she suddenly broke into a dance. She hurled herself around the room causing the knight to step nimbly out of her way as he drained the drink. He put down the stowp, thanked the woman and left.

'What are you up to?' he enquired of the laird.

Whiteford gave a shrug and feigned innocence. 'Sall we wag awa on oor hunt an aiblins back-come in a wee bittie?' As they passed a group of farm workers walking towards the cottage Whiteford gave a snort of laughter then quickly composed himself.

Two hours later, with a small deer across their pack horse, the hunters returned to the cottage. The laird allowed Sir Thomas to go before him. When Wallace entered, to his amazement and amusement the farm workers and the woman were dancing wildly round the room. He started to laugh, then, to his horror, suddenly found he had the urge to join the dancers. At that moment the laird withdrew the pin and fixed it to his lapel. and Sir Thomas and the dancers lost the urge to hurl themselves around the room. The woman quickly went to her bucket and filled two pint stowps and handed them to the hunters. The laird looked her in the eye, 'Yer coo deed o colic frae muckle spring gress, your dug deed o auld age, yer bairn is noo eleeven and will rin wild fer anither pickle o years then settle doon. As tae your kirn: wipe the butter aff your fingers afore liftin it.'

The woman curtsied, 'Aye sir, a'll tak yer advice. Thank ye.'

LAIRD O FAIL AND THE PACKMAN

On a fine summer's day Sir Thomas and the laird were taking a pleasant stroll along the banks of Ayr, when a packman leading a donkey laden with creels full of crockery passed along the track on the opposite bank. 'A wager a can mak that man smash aa his dishes,' said the laird.

'Dinnae be rideeculous man. A hawker widnae smash his wares.'

'A wager he daes itherwise.'

'The wager is taen,' said Sir Thomas.

They looked back over the river and the hawker stopped and undid the ropes of his panniers which dropped on to the ground and scattered broken dishes in all directions. The hawker stood awhile gazing at the disaster before gathering up all the pieces placing them in the creels and tying them back on the donkey. He continued on his way.

'Ye ken,' said Sir Thomas, 'a am an ass masel. A shuidnae hae taen the wager. Noo that puir fella is withoot a leevin.'

'Nae sic a thing,' said the laird. 'When he gets tae the mercat in Ayr, he'll fin aa his gear in ae piece again.'

'Sae aa that grief fer a cheap wager. Ye hae nae hert, ma freen.'

'Aye a dae; fer ye see, in ilka caup there wis a demon wi the heid o a dug and it wis aboot tae put a cantrip on the man. He'd hae drappit deid afore he walkit anither mile. A juist saufed his life.'

Sir Thomas raised an eyebrow as if to question the truth of the laird's statement. The serious eye that was returned told him that his friend was indeed true to his word.

THE LAIRD O FAIL AND THE ROWAN

Sir Thomas Wallace paid another visit to see Walter Whiteford in the autumn of the same year. Sir Thomas enjoyed a brandy with the laird while looking out of the upper south window of Fail Castle. Together they counted twenty ploughs at work on the runrigs that spread out before them. Each of the ploughs had a team of eight oxen to haul it. Each rig had a ploughman, a horse leader and a lad or lass with a pole to push the coulter, or cutter, back into the ground when it hit a stone and bounced out. It was hard work and done in all weathers. 'It's a gran sicht,' said Sir Thomas, 'but tirin work.'

'Aye tis,' agreed the laird, 'Aiblins they suid tak a wee break. In fact, a'll wager ye a can halt the progress o aa they teams.'

'Whit wuid ye wager?' said Wallace.

'A hunner Scots poonds.'

'Aa twinty o them?'

'Them aa.'

'Ye're on.'

The men shook hands, then the laird took a step to the window and opened it. Sir Thomas watched his friend as he stood utterly motionless his eyes fixed on his quarry; the team stopped. The laird remained quite still but his eyes had moved to another target. One by one the teams stopped until there were only two still ploughing. Whiteford increased his concentration but to no avail. Eventually he admitted defeat.

'A'm impressed wi ye man. That wis some feat tae perform. Wuid the Deil no help ye wi the last we bit.'

'It wisnae the Deil that helpit me. It wis the pooer o ma ain mind. If a wis helpit, it wis the Guid Lord hissel, an him that stoppit me, as only He kens perfitness. Noo gin ye haud on a meenit, a'll get yer money.'

After the laird had paid his dues, he and Sir Thomas walked out to the two teams that had not stopped at his behest. On arriving at them he noticed that each had a garland of rowan leaves lashed to the handles. 'A think a see the problem,' said the laird. 'The rowantree seems to interfere with my mind vibrations.'

'It also keeps the witches and warlocks awa,' said Sir Thomas, with an impertinent grin.

'Hae mind or a'll turn ye intae a puddock,' replied the laird, with a wicked grin.

FAIL FAILS

Sorcerer or not, the life of the Laird of Fail came to an end. On his death bed he cautioned everyone to keep him unburied until after the harvest, as a great storm would arise on that day. He also demanded that once his body had left the castle no one was to return there, on pain of death. Although the harvest was half done, the odour of his decaying body became unbearable so that his family was forced to bury him. As his body was interred the great storm broke causing widespread damage to the remaining undone harvest. Sheaves were scattered beyond saving and haywains were thrown over and damaged. The storm raged on for days until the roof of Fail Castle collapsed. Had anyone not heeded the laird's warning to leave it, they would surely have been killed. So ended the life of an unusual man who, though feared as a warlock, was in truth a good and kindly man with an occasional wicked sense of humour.

57

The Wee Bunnock

The following tale is well known as the Gingerbread Man and there are many other versions of it across Scotland, even in Gaelic. The following version is found in 'Chamber's Popular Rhymes of Scotland', published in 1826. It was told by an aged woman in Symington, Ayrshire, who died in 1789 at the age of eighty-four, and was recorded word-for-word from her grandson and remains so in this version. An English translation is printed below it.

There lived an auld man and an auld wife at the side o' a burn. They had twa kye, five hens and a cock, a cat and twa kittlins. The auld man lookit after the kye, and the auld wife span on the tow rock. The kittlins aft grippit at the auld wife's spindle, as it tussled ower the hearth-stane.

'Sho, sho,' she wad say, 'gae wa,' and so it tussled about. Ae day, after parritch-time, she thought she wad hae a bunnock. Sae she bakit twa aitmeal bunnocks and set them to the fire to harden. After a while, the auld man cam in, and sat down aside the fire, and taks ane o the bunnocks, an snappit it through the middle. When the tither ane sees this, it rins aff as fast as it could, and the auld wife after't, wi the spindle in the ae hand and the tow rock in the tither. But the wee bunnock wan awa, and out o sicht, and ran till it cam to a gude muckle thack house, and ben it ran boldly to the fireside; and there were three tailors sitting on a muckle table.

When they saw the wee bunnock come ben, they jumpit up, and gat in ahint the gudewife, that was cardin tow ayont the fire. 'Hout,' quo she, 'be na fleyt; it's but a wee bunnock. Grip it, and I'll gie ye a soup milk till't.' Up she gets wi' the tow-cards, and the tailor wi the goose, and the twa prentices, the ane wi the muckle shears and the tither wi the lawbrod; but it jinkit them and ran roun about the fire and ane o the prentices, thinking to snap it wi the shears, fell i the asepit. The tailor cuist the goose, and the gudewife the tow-cards; but at wadna do. The bunnock wan awa, and ran till it cam to a wee house at the roadside; and in it rins, and there was a weaver sittin on the loom, and the wife winnin a clue o yarn. 'Tibby,' quo he, 'what's tat ?' 'Oh,' quo she, 'it's a wee bunnock.'

'It's weel come,' quo he, 'for our sowens were but thin the day. Grip it, my woman, grip it.'

'Ay,' quo she; 'what recks! That's a clever bunnock. Kep, Willie; kep, man.'

'Hout,' quo Willie, 'cast the clue at it.' But the bunnock whipit roun about, and but the floor, and aff it gaed, and ower the knowe, like a new-tarred sheep, or a daft yell cow. And forrit it runs to the neist house, and ben to the fireside. And there was the gudewife kirnin. 'Come awa, wee bunnock,' quo she; 'I'se hae ream and bread the day.' But the wee bunnock whipit roun about the kirn, and the wife after't, and i the hurry she had near-hand coupit the kirn. And afore she got it set richt again, the wee bunnock was aff, and down the brae to the mill. And in it ran. The miller was siftin meal i' the trough; but, looking up, 'Ay,' quo' he, 'it's a sign o' plenty when ye're rinnin about, and naebody to look after ye. But I like a bunnock and cheese. Come your wa's ben, and I'll gie ye a nicht's quarters.' But the bunnock wadna trust itself wi' the miller and his cheese. Sae it turned and ran its wa's out; but the millar didna fash his head wi't.

So, it toddled awa', and ran till it cam to the smithy. And in it rins, and up to the studdy. The smith was making horse-nails. Quo' he, 'I like a bicker o' gude yill and a weel-toastit bunnock. Come your wa's in by here.' But the bunnock was frightened when it heard about the yill; and turned and aff as hard as it could, and the smith after't, and cuist the hammer. But it whirlt awa', and out o' sight in a crack, and ran till it cam to a farm-house, wi' a gude muckle peat-stack at the end o't. Ben it rins to the fireside.

The gudeman was clovin lint, and the gudewife hecklin. 'Oh, Janet,' quo' he, 'there's a wee bunnock ; I'se hae the hauf o't.'

'Weel, John, I'se hae the tither

hauf. Hit it ower the back wi' the clove.' But the bunnock playt *jink-about*. 'Hout, tout,' quo' the wife, and gart the heckle flee at it. But it was ower clever for her. And aff and up the burn it ran, to the neist house, and whirlt its wa's ben to the fireside. The gudewife was stirrin the sowens, and the gudeman plettin spret-binnings for the kye. 'Ho, Jock,' quo' the gudewife, 'come here. Thou's aye cryin' about a wee bunnock. Here's ane. Come in, haste ye, and I'll help thee to grip it.'

'Ay, mither, whaur is't ?'

'See there. Rin ower o' that side.' But the bunnock ran in ahint the gudeman's chair. Jock fell amang the sprets. The gudeman cuist a binning, and the gudewife the spurtle. But it was ower clever for Jock and her baith. It was aff and out o' sight in a crack, and through among the whins, and down the road to the neist house, and in, and ben to the fireside.

The folk were just sittin down to their sowens, and the gudewife scartin the pat. 'Losh!' quo' she, 'there's a wee bunnock come in to warm itself at our fireside.'

'Steek the door,' quo' the gudeman, 'And we'll try to get a grip o't.' When the bunnock heard that, it ran but the house, and they after't wi' their spunes, and the gudeman cuist his bunnat. But it whirlt awa', and ran, and better ran, till it cam to another house. And when it gaed ben, the folk were just gaun to their beds. The gudeman was castin aff his breeks, and the gudewife rakin the fire. 'What's tat?' quo' he.

'Oh,' quo' she, 'it's a wee bunnock.'

Quo' he, 'I could eat the hauf o't, for a' the brose I hae suppit.'

'Grip it,' quo' the wife, 'and I'll hae a bit too.'

'Cast your breeks at it—kep—kep!' The gudeman cuist the breeks and had near hand smoor't it. But it warsl't out, and ran, and the gudeman after't, wantin the breeks. And there was a clean chase ower the craft park, and up the wunyerd, and in amang the whins. And the gudeman lost it, and had to come his wa's trottin' hame hauf nakit.

But now it was grown dark, and the wee bunnock couldna see; but it gaed into the side o' a muckle whin bush, and into a tod's hole. The tod had gotten nae meat for twa days. 'Oh, welcome, welcome,' quo' the tod, and snappit it in twa i' the middle. And that was the end o' the wee bunnock.

[At the conclusion, Grannie would look round upon her little audience, and add the following, by way of moral:

'Now, weans, an ye live to grow muckle, be na ower lifted up about ony thing, nor ower sair cuisten down; for ye see the folk were aa cheated, and the puir tod got the bunnock.']

ae – one; *aspit* – ash pit of the fire; *bicker* – beaker; *breeks* – trousers; *brose* – cooked barley, water butter and salt; *cardin*: brushing; *clovin* – cutting; *clue* (wool) – ball; *craft* – croft; *cuist* – cast; *fash* – worry; *flyt* – scared; *forrit* – forward; *goose* – tailor's smoothing iron; *hauf* – half; heckling -brushing; *kittlins* – kittens; *kye* - cows; *lawbrod* – board laid on the knees; *muckle* – big; *neist*- next; *ower* – over; *parritch* – porridge; *pat* – pot; *plettin*: plaiting; *recks* – reckon; *scartin* – scraping; *smoor* – smother; *sowens*: oatmeal drink; *spret-binnings*- reed rope; *spune* – spoon; *steek* – shut; *thack* – thatch; *tod* – fox; *tow rock*- a device to hold the combed wool before spinning; *warsl't* – wrestled; *weans* – (wee ones) children; *whins* – gorse; *wunyerd* – corn-drying yard; *yell cow* – barren/not pregnant;

THE WEE BANNOCK

There lived an old man and an old wife at the side of a stream. They had two cows, five hens, a cockerel, a cat and two kittens. The old man looked after the cows and the old wife spun wool from a distaff. The kittens often grabbed the spindle as it spun above the hearthstone. 'Shoo! Shoo! She would say, 'Go away!'

One day after breakfast she thought she would make bannocks, oatmeal cakes. She baked two and set them by the fire to harden. After a while the old man came in and sat down beside the fire, he took one of the cakes and broke it through the middle. When the other saw this it ran off as fast as it could and the old wife after it with the spindle in one hand and the distaff in the other.

The wee bannock ran away and out of sight. It ran until it came to a fine thatched house. It boldly ran into the sitting room and up by the fireside where there were three tailors sitting at a large table. When they saw the bannock come in, they jumped up and hid behind the good wife who was combing wool on the other side of the fire. 'Hoots,' she said, 'Don't be scared, it's but a wee bannock. Catch it and I'll give you some milk to go with it.' Up she gets with the brushed wool and the tailor with his smoothing iron and the two apprentices, one with the big scissors and the other with his lap-board, but it avoided them and ran around the fire. One of the apprentices, thinking to snap it with the scissors, fell in the ashpit. The tailor threw the iron and the goodwife the wool, but that did no good.

The wee bannock was away and ran until it came to a house at the roadside and in it ran and there was a weaver sitting at his loom and his wife winding a ball of wool. 'Tibby,' said he, 'What's that?'

'Oh!' said she, 'It's a wee bannock.'

'It's welcome,' said he, 'for our sowens are a bit thin today. Catch it my woman, catch it.'

'Yes,' said she, 'What does it matter! That's a clever wee bannock. Catch it, Willie; catch it, man.'

'Hoots,' said Willie. 'Cast the wool at it.' But the bannock whipped round about and dived on to the floor and off it went over the hill like a new-tarred sheep or a daft dry, cow.

And forward it ran to the next house and into the fireside. And there was a goodwife churning butter. 'Come away wee bannock,' said she, 'I'll have cream and bread today.' But the wee bannock whipped round about the butter churn with the wife after it, and in her hurry nearly toppled the churn. Before she got it set right again, the wee bannock was off and down the hill to the mill.

In it ran. The miller was sifting meal in a trough, but looking up 'Yes,' said he, 'it's a sign of plenty when you are running about and nobody to look after you. But I like a bannock and cheese. Come your way in and I'll give you a night's lodgings.' But the bannock wouldn't trust itself with the miller and his cheese. So, it turned and ran its way out. But the miller didn't bother his head with it.

So, it toddled away and ran until it came to a smithy. And in it runs and up to the anvil. The smith was making nails for horseshoes. Said he, 'I like a beaker of ale and a wee toasted bannock. Come your way in by here.' But the bannock was frightened when it heard about the ale and was off as hard as it could and the smith after it. He threw his hammer. But it whirled away and out of sight in a crack.

It ran until it came to a farmhouse with a great stack of peat against the gable end. In it runs to the fireside. The goodman was beating flax and the goodwife was combing it. 'Oh Janet,' said he, 'There's a wee bannock. I'll have half of it.'

'Well John, I'll have the other half. Hit it over the back with the beater.' But the wee bannock played dodge. 'Hoot, toot,' said the wife, and threw the comb at it. But it was too clever for her and off up the stream it ran.

It ran to the next house and whirled its way into the fireside. The goodwife was stirring the sowens and the goodman plaiting reed-rope for the cows. 'Ho Jock,' said the goodwife, 'You're always going on about a wee bannock. Here's one. Come quickly and I'll help you catch it.'

'Yes mother, where is it?'

'See there. Run over to that side.' But the bannock ran behind the goodman's chair. Jock fell among the reeds. The goodman threw a rope and the goodwife the stirring-stick. But it was too clever for Jock and her both. It was off and out of sight in a crack and through among the gorse bushes.

It went down the road to the next house and into the fireside. The people were just sitting down to their sowens and the goodwife scraping the pot, 'Losh,' said she, 'there's a wee bannock come in to warm itself at our fireside.'

'Shut the door,' said the goodman, 'and we'll try to get a hold of it.' When the wee bannock heard this, it ran to the outer room and they after it with their spoons and the goodman threw his cap. But it whirled away and ran and better ran until it came to another house.

When it went in, the people were just going to their beds. The goodman was taking off his trousers and the goodwife was raking the fire. 'What's that?' said he.

'Oh,' said she, 'it's a wee bannock.'

Said he, 'I could eat the half of it, for all the brose I have supped.'

'Catch it,' said the wife, and I'll have a bit too. Throw your trousers at it. Catch! Catch!' The goodman threw his trousers and nearly smothered it, but it wrestled out and ran, the goodman after it wanting his trousers. There was a chase over the field, up the corn-drying yard and in among the gorse. The goodman lost it and had to trot home half naked.

It was now grown dark and the wee bannock could not see, but it went into a big gorse bush and into a fox's hole. The fox had no food for two days. 'Oh welcome. Welcome,' said the fox and snapped it in two in the middle. And that was the end of the wee bannock.

Now be ye lords or commoners,
Ye needna laugh nor sneer,
Fer ye'll aa be i the tod's hole,
In less than a hunner year.

The above is an almost exact translation from the Scots. A few Scots words have been left in as there is no equivalent in English. Sowens is made by putting oats in water and letting it sit for a week. The liquid is then drained and compressed and allowed to settle – give the meal to the chickens. A thick glutinous mass forms at the bottom and this is the sowens. The liquid, which is sour, but probiotic, can be drunk. Sowens can be heated and butter added to taste or the 'cream' put on your scones. Tastes a lot better than it sounds. Brose is also made from oats (like most ancient Scottish meals). You can add hot milk or water to it, throw in salt and butter, give a quick rough stir and away you go. It can also be made from barley (barley brose) but takes longer to cook. Both are delicious. Losh is an interjection like 'Good Grief' or such. It is really what is called a 'deformation' of the word Lord, as Gosh is for God. The Scots version to Scots speakers and admirers is a pure delight. Had it been written, many of the repetitions would have been removed (though repetition is important in folk tales) to spark it up. However, this is an exact copy of the way it was told, and orally the unnecessary and duller repetitions are not noticed.

58

The Wicked Laird o Culzean

Atween Wigton and the toun o Ayr,
Portpatrick and the Cruives o Cree,
Nae man need think for to bide there,
Unless he court wi Kennedie.

It is said that the Kennedy clan are descendants of the ancient British tribes that inhabited southern Scotland in the Dark Ages. It is speculated that the name derives from Cunnedda, a leader of the Votadini of Lothian, who was sent to the South-West to counter Pictish and Scottish insurgents into the area. More likely is that it comes from Gaelic where the first part is from Ceann meaning, literally, head, as in chieftain. The second half of the name might come from helmet or, more likely, eidigh meaning fierce. Whatever the truth is, one thing is for sure, as can be seen from the old rhyme, they ruled the South-West with fists of iron.

While they are regarded as people of their time, one in particular stands out as a nasty piece of work: Sir Archibald Kennedy, 1st Baronet of Culzean, born around 1636. While power played a part in his design, greed also formed his soul. Using legal and political power and the subtle threat of violence, he manoeuvred small landowners in Carrick into signing over the rights to their land. When he died in 1710 a strange boat with a fiery glow was seen on the Firth of Clyde. When hailed by a passing boat, 'From whence to where?' a voice replied, 'From Hell to Culzean'. When the funeral cortege was about to depart a crow alighted on the hearse and though heavily encouraged, the horses would not move until finally the corbie flew away. All who beheld it knew that the Devil had come to claim his own.

59

William Wallace and the Barns of Ayr

Edward I of England was a superb fighter and warrior as well as an astute politician; but he was a man for whom enough was never enough. After the accidental death of the Scots king, Alexander III, he engineered himself into the position of judge as to who would be the future King of Scots. Purposely, he chose the weakest of the contenders, John Baliol, knowing he could easily manipulate him. This did not sit well with the Scots ruling aristocracy and Baliol was deposed due to his ineffectiveness; a council of twelve was then set up to govern the country. The council also established a treaty with France against King Edward; this is still referred to this day as The Auld Alliance. Edward was unamused and promptly invaded Scotland – his intent all along – and defeated the Scottish forces at the Battle of Dunbar. A key figure in the ensuing Wars of Independence was one William Wallace, born at either Elderslie, near Paisley or, as some assert, at Ellerslie near Kilmarnock.

The duplicitous Edward first carried out a war of attrition then offered a truce to the freedom fighters, or whom he considered to be rebels. Keen to have peace in the land, the nobles agreed to a parliament with the English. A meeting was arranged in Ayr at the town barns that stood beside the river. Among those attending were Sir Ronald Crawford, Sheriff of Ayr and uncle of William Wallace, Sir Bryce Blair of Blair, Sir Neil Montgomerie of Cassillis and Sir Hugh Montgomerie. On arrival, they were asked to enter the building in pairs. In rank Sir Ronald and Sir Bryce entered first. Inside they were accosted by armed English soldiers, and without due process were gagged tied and hung by the neck from the barn's beams. Each pair entering suffered the same fate. A peasant woman watched the proceedings, then ran pell-mell to warn late arrivals. The lesser nobility including Wallace made their way to the meeting but were held up because Braveheart was attending to an errand on behalf of his uncle. As he arrived at the Woodgate, the woman came running up the street towards him, 'Hold, hold brave Wallace. There is English treachery and the nobles are hanged like dogs in the Barns of Ayr.'

Realising that a head-on attack would serve little purpose, except in killing more Scots, Wallace bided his time. That night the enemy soldiers revelled in their vile deed, celebrating with local beer; finally, they fell into a drunken sleep. The patient Scots crept up on the barns and chained the doors, Next, they carried armfuls of straw and piled it against the wooden building and threw on flaming torches. In no time the straw was ablaze and then the building itself. Those inside made to get out the doors but found them barred. In desperation they hacked at the wooden walls and some made it through only to be impaled on spear and sword, the rest were driven back until the blazing structure collapsed on all within. Wallace and his band then headed south to the Carrick Hills to a place now known as Wallace's Seat. In the distance he could see the conflagration, and as his men joined him to view their handiwork, he said, 'The Barns o Ayr burn weel.'

Another tale says that as well as the barns, the English were also garrisoned in the town. As they settled for the night, the woman passed through the town painting white crosses on the houses; these Wallace also set ablaze. The deed went into history as the Black Parliament. It is also said that some of the English were garrisoned at the local monastery. When the Prior heard of Wallace's actions, he bade the monks arm themselves and they slew the invaders. This was locally known as the Friars of Ayr's Blessing.

Grim times indeed.

60

The Witch of Auchenmade

Nanny Pollock was indeed a witch and fond of helping folks she liked but making a misery of the lives of those who she had taken a 'doon-heid' to. Unfortunately for the farmer at Merryhiggen, it was the latter. She cast a glamour on his cattle so that they largely dried up of milk. What little was obtained was no better than skimmed milk and no-matter how long it was churned, would produce no butter. On the verge of ruination, the farmer sought the help of a spey-wife who was versed in such matters. 'Whit has causit this Mrs Smith?'

'A glaumerie has been cuist on yer kye.'

'Wha wuid hae duin sic a diablolical thing?'

'There's only yin hereaboots, an that is Nan Pollock o Auchenmade.'

'Naw!'

'Aye!'

Thinkin on it, A had a faa oot wi her no langsyne.'

'She suid hae been brunt, that bluidy limb o sorrow,' said the woman.

'Whit can ye dae?'

'Weel, ye'll hae tae bring aa yer kye intae the byre, an while ye are aboot that, a'll steek up aa the holes. We dinnae want her cuistin a glaumer on us while we are aboot oor business.'

Merryhiggen went off to bring in the cows from the outbye fields while the speywife stuffed straw into all the holes and cracks she could find. Satisfied she had done a good job, the wise-woman set a fire going in against an end wall. From it she lit a candle she kept in her pocket and set it in a nook in the wall where a stone had fallen out. The smoke rose from the burning straw and peat and drifted upwards, leaking through the thatch. She then went over to the farmhouse and obtained a pot and a small milk-can from the goodwife. She put in a little spring water in each, returned to the fire and placed the

pot on top. As the eighteen cows entered, she shooed them to the other end. When they were all in, the farmer closed the door. With only the light of a candle she walked among them, making a tiny slit in their hindquarters and extracting a little blood which she scraped into the small milk can. She then took the blood and poured it into the now boiling water, making sure she had scraped it all from the can. Soon water and blood were bubbling with heat. She removed it and set it on the floor. After a few minutes she put it on again for two minutes and brought it to the boil. She continued to do that as the farmer looked on with ever growing curiosity.

'Whit will happen?' he asked.

'Ye'll see,' was all she said.

Suddenly, there was a banging at the door. 'Ur ye in there, Merryhiggen?'

The speywife held a finger to her mouth to shush him, looking over at the door where a tiny point of light shone through a nailhole, 'Damn, misst that,' she whispered to herself. She hoped it was small enough to hold out glaumerie.

The banging became more frantic, 'Can ye hear me man?'

Mrs Smith put the pot back on the fire. A moment later there was a howl from outside the door, 'Wuid ye tak the pat aff the lowe, ma hert is bylin.'

'No until ye tak yer glaumerie aff the coos,' called the speywife, letting the pot boil furiously.

There was a scream of pure agony, 'A wull! A wull!'

'Dae it.'

There was a pause, 'Tis duin.'

Mrs Smith went over to a cow and gave a long pull on a teat. A thick stream of warm fresh milk streamed on to the floor. She walked back to the pot and removed it and poured the cold water from the milk-can into it. She then walked over to the door and opened it, 'Gin a hear o ye causin mischief hereaboots, there wull be worse fer ye.'

The farmer came out, his face all suppressed fury. 'Aye bugger aff afore a pit ma fit tae yer erse.' The Witch of Auchenmade made a hasty retreat and Merryhiggen was never bothered again. As for Mrs Smith: she had a quart of milk and a big pat of butter delivered to her door every week.

61

Witch or Wise Woman

Bessie Dunlop never thought of herself as a witch. She was a good Christian woman, attended church every Sunday and was considerate to her neighbours. The only broom she owned was for sweeping the floor of her tidily kept house and the family cat was tiger-striped and lazy. As for a cauldron: nothing unusual in that. Everyone had one that hung from a cleik or hook in the chimney or from a rafter, if the fire was in the middle of the floor, as was common. Perhaps it was her innocence that drew in other-worldly forces.

One day in the year 1574, while in the kailyard washing linen clothes in a wooden tub, she was approached by a kindly-looking gentleman. Grey-bearded and elderly, his clothes seemed a little dated, though the very few gentlemen who lived into old age were known to wear such attire: a jerkin with slashed sleeves over a blouson shirt and a ruff at the neck, breeches and silk stocking than ended half way up the thigh with a garter. On his head was a velvet bonnet and, in his hand, he carried a wand of ivy bleached white. Curious as she was, she had no desire to engage in conversation due to feeling distraught at her circumstances. He looked at her kindly, 'Guid day Bessie. Whit ails ye lass?'

'Daes it shaw?'

'Aye.'

'Weel, a hae cause tae be sad: ma man's no weel, ma bairnie is deein an we hae little warldy gear left.'

'Weel, let me tell ye Bessie: Yer bairnie wull dee, as wull yer coo an twa yowes; but yer man will thrive, sae ye maun greet an rejoice thegither.'

'Wha ur ye?' enquired Bessie.

'A am Thomas Reid an a wis killt at the Battle o Pinkie in September o 1547. Noo I reside in the Coort o the Queen o Elfhame.' He looked at her long and steady, 'Tis a place ye wuid be maist welcome.'

'Amang the fairy folk?'

'Aye.'

'But a'm no deid.'

'Maks nae difference tae the guidfolk.'

'Whit aboot ma man?'

'He'd be welcome tae and he'll neer be ill in Elfland.'

'Ye're offer is temptin, sir, but a hae tae decline.' Bessie dropped her head with embarrassment. 'Tis against ma beliefs, sir.'

'Then discard ye're beliefs lass. They hae duin ye nae service, nor will they serve ye in the weeks tae come.'

Bessie could not argue against the charges, yet her belief was staunch and would not be changed. 'A trust i the Lord, sir, an accept his judgement on me.'

'An whit heinous crime has a lass like ye perpetrated on humankind tae deserve sic a puinishment?'

Bessie dropped her head and refused to comment.

'Think on it, lass. Think hard on it.' Thomas Reid turned about and walked towards a drystane dyke. Though he was all of five feet six inches tall he disappeared with ease through a lunkey hole that was no more than two feet six inches high. Bessie stared on in disbelief.

True to the prophecy, Bessie's child, her cow and two ewes died, and her husband recovered from his fever. She was distraught at her loss but relieved that her husband had not succumbed to his ailment. Shortly afterwards Thomas Reid returned and remonstrated with her for not trusting in him. 'Gie up yer religion lass an jyne me in the land o everlastin youth. Dae ye no trust me?'

'A wuid trust in onybody that wuid dae me guid.'

'Then trust in me, gie up yer beliefs an cam wae me tae Elfland. Ye sal hae horses, kye, an as mony yowes an aa the graith that ye'd want.'

'Aa these things a wuid wish, but I wuid be riven in twa afore a gied up ma faith.'

Reid raged at her for her decision and stamped off in the huff.

Some days later he returned in a better mood and pressed her to accompany him. They walked a little way to a shaw on Caff Water where he introduced her to four men and eight women. 'These guid folks are frae Elfland and they wuid hae words wae ye.' A picnic was set out with strange fruits and sweetmeats she had never before seen. They treated her graciously

and offered her cordials of wild fruits and flowers which stunned her taste buds. Encouraged by the group she tried the food and found it highly agreeable and unlike anything she had ever tasted before. She was quite giddy with it all and laughed with delight. 'See Bessie, aa this is the common fare o Elfhame and yours if ye wuid but gie up yer faith an jyne us.'

'A am set in ma weys, an ma faith is solid,' she said.

At this Thomas Reid and the company departed, a harsh wind blowing suddenly in their wake.

Reid returned shortly afterwards. 'A dinnae unnerstaun ye Bessie.'

'But if a gang wi ye, hou am a tae ken whit will become o me?'

'Luik at me lass, a've been deid these past thirty years or so an a am hale an herty, an brankie forby.'

Though wholly resistant to Reid's overtures, Bessie Dunlop still acquainted with him and sought his advice on many matters: what herbs cured what illnesses, was a husband or wife faithful, where might a lost possession be found? All this and more, and as a result Bessie gained a reputation as a woman of great wisdom, which she enjoyed and encouraged. Reid always seemed to appear when she needed him, but she also saw him once at a funeral in Dalry churchyard and another time in Edinburgh. In each case he comported himself as if he were just another human being, which she thought strange. As for the fairy folk, she had little contact with them except once when a well-built woman suddenly appeared as she was drinking water from her hands and begged that she share the liquid. The woman then prophesied that Bessie would lose another child, which she did. Reid said that it was the Queen of Elfhame herself come to pay a visit. She also encountered a band of riders near Edinburgh who disappeared into Restalrig Loch. Reid confirmed to her that they were on the Fairy Rade. Along with them, she said, was the Warlock Laird of Auchenskeith

The Witchcraft Act of Scotland had been instituted a few years before and it was only a matter of time before Bessie would become embroiled with it. For some time, she had been protected by helping people from the aristocracy and merchant class. However, William Kyle, Burgess of the town, approached her regarding a cloak belonging to Hugh Scott. Bessie indicated that the cloak had been thieved by Mally Boyd who had reworked it into a garment known as a kirtle, a kind of outer petticoat. Unable to prove the theft, Kyle had Bessie arrested on witchcraft charges. She was released through the help of a powerful acquaintance, James Blair. But it was the circumstances over the theft of plough irons that led to her demise. Bessie named blacksmiths Gabriel and George Black as the culprits. Through the bribing of a sheriff's officer, William Dougal, the items were disappeared, and Bessie was now the target. A witchfinder or Skeillie Man was sent for, who did the usual horrific investigations to prove her guilt: looking for marks of the Devil, and slashing her above the mouth (scored abune the breath). Goodness only knows what other atrocities were perpetrated on this poor soul. In the end Bessie, who had never been associated with the Devil or ever been accused of hurting anyone, was taken to Dalkeith, found guilty of witchcraft and sentenced to be strangled and burnt on Castle Hill in Edinburgh. There is no record of the execution, but her fate is almost certain.

62
The Wraith of Joseph Black

Joseph Black was a miner and though he lived at Grievehill, New Cumnock, he preferred to practise his religion in Sanquhar. Every Sunday, Dr Simpson, minister of the North United Presbyterian Church, would see Joseph at both the morning and evening services. As the round journey was twenty miles his journey home was usually after dark. It was one such Sunday evening as the miner was walking home past Gateside he was taken by surprise at a figure who appeared beside him; he had not been aware of his approach nor heard any footsteps. The fact that the figure seemed more to glide than walk perturbed him even more. His immediate thought was that it was his shadow, then realised that the moon was behind the figure. He also noticed that the person was dressed exactly like himself with a suit, bonnet and plaidie. The presence remained with him from Brunthouse near Wellstrand all the way to Bank Wood, when it seemed to fade to nothing.

At home, Joseph related the story to his wife, after which they had supper and retired to bed. In the middle of the night there was a house-shaking crash, as if a wall had collapsed. Joseph leaped from his bed to investigate, only to find that all was as it should be. Mystified, he returned to bed and he and his wife drifted back into sleep. Perhaps an hour later there was another crash, as if the kitchen shelf had collapsed and their crockery had smashed on the floor. Again, after investigation, there was nothing untoward.

Now unable to sleep, both rose, said their morning prayers, and prepared breakfast. After kissing his wife goodbye, Joseph went to work at the mine. He was hacking into a seam when the ceiling collapsed and buried him completely. He was dug out alive, but his back was broken. He died shortly afterwards. His widow was sure that the stranger on the road from Sanquhar was Joseph's own wraith and the crash was a portend of how he would die.

63

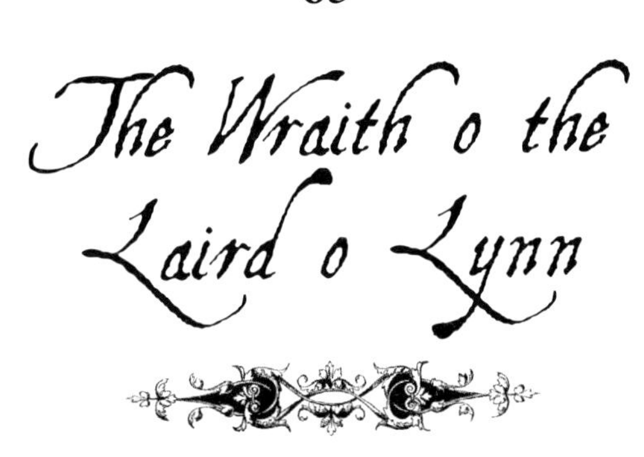

The young Laird of Lynn called for his retainers to saddle his fine, black hunter, loose the hounds and prepare to ride out on the hunt. As they did so, other riders appeared and the cohort set off at a fast trot, hounds crying and horns blowing. As they trooped away, Lady Lynn, mother of the young laird, set out on her daily constitutional walk. It was always her joy to wander down the Lynn Glen. The air was freshened by woodland and the rush of running water and she adored its music. With her she took a small charcoal stick and a booklet in which she scribbled her musings. It was easy to write surrounded by, what she called, a 'simple grandeur'. It was a place of refuge, a sanctuary after the death of her beloved husband. Her favourite place was a rock beside a larger rock near a spout, or waterfall, that served as a seat with a backrest. Here she drew her cloak about her, closed her eyes and let the rush of the water slip her into reverie.

It was on such a day, as she sat deep in meditation, that something dark stirred in the depths of her being. Her eyes opened in alarm and it was then she saw the buck running, as if for its life. It passed behind a bush at the bottom of a vertical cliff and disappeared. On its trail came a pack of slavering hounds in pursuit, followed by riders, one blowing on a horn. The Lady stared in an awe that turned to dread, for though there was a great visual commotion, not a sound was heard from the chase. What unnerved her most was that the leader of the band was her own son. They followed the path of the stag and vanished into the cliff-face.

Alarmed and near fainting from the vision, Lady Lynne hurried home.

She arrived and waited for the return of the hunt. The hours seemed as days until, at last, she heard the ring of hooves on the cobbles. She rushed out and greeted the company. All seemed safe and well and she placed her hand upon her breast and let out a great sigh of relief when she saw her son.

'Whit a merry time we had, ower muir an hill,' he said, 'an a gran buck tae croun it. Ha! Ha!' He stopped mid-laugh, 'Mither, ye luik unweel. Whit ails ye?'

'A will tell ye later.'

After supper, they retired the servants for the evening and settled themselves by the great fireplace. 'Nou mither, tell me. Ye ate little and yer face has paled, een in the firelicht.'

She covered her face with her hands and gave a low whimper. The laird rose from his chair, knelt beside her and took her hands from her face. He looked into her sad, grey eyes, 'Is it faither?'

'No, ma son. It is ye.'

'But a am weel,' he said throwing his arms wide.

She cocked her head, gave a sad smile and took his face in her hands, 'And sae ye are,' she said in a voice heavy with sorrow.

'Sae why the daurksome een?'

'Because these een hae seen a vision; a forebodin o…o.' She stopped and looked long and hard into his eyes, 'a saw ye in the neist warld: Ye were ridin through Lynn Glen at the heid o a spectral companie.'

'A wis ridin wae a ghastly bunch o comrades.' He laughed at his own joke.

'But a ken whit a saw, an ye were aa phantasms.'

'Mither, nane o us kens the day o oor daith, which is fortunate. And een if whit ye saw is o the morra or the neist day, then God has chosen ma time. He gave me the gift o life, and ma life is his to tak when he chooses. A hae nae fear, for a trust in his guidness.' He took her hands in his and squeezed them, 'Aa that a wuid dreid is that ye are left tae mourn. But dinnae dae that, if only for ma sake. A will *dree ma weird*, as ye maun.' She nodded.

Next morning the Laird was up early. He saddled and bridled his horse and went out for a long morning ride. By mid-afternoon he had still not returned, and search parties went out looking for him. It was just after sunset when the stable boy saw his horse among the trees in Lynn Glen. He called the chief steward who found his body lying in the pool below the Lynn Spout.

The man carried the body of his laird, placed it on the long table in the hallway and stepped back weeping. Lady Lynn entered, her face lined and with the look of a broken woman. 'Whaur did ye fin him?'

'In the Lynn Pool, Milady, ablow the sheer rock face, juist whaur ye hae yer seat. He must hae slipped aff the edge' The steward looked at his mistress, 'Why wuid he gang there?'

He was too late to catch her as she fell.

64

YOUNG ROBIN AND THE HEADLESS HORSE AND HORSEMAN

In the Scotland of the past, people who went from door to peddling or hawking goods often had the title of 'cadger'. One such cadger had the nickname Young Robin though, in truth he was greying at the temple or, as was said in the Scots language, 'His haffets were lyart an grey'. One darkening evening with a bright gibbous moon, as Young Robin returned home from plying his trade in Kilmarnock, he became aware of a presence, and looking to his side saw that a silent rider and horse were accompanying him. All good and well, except that his companions were both headless. Robin, in fright, spurred his horse and raced homeward. But no matter how fast he rode, the headless ghouls kept pace with him. With his mind solely on reaching his home village Robin lowered his head further and urged his nag on with the aid of a whip. Fortunately for Robin, but especially for his poor horse, they thundered across a bridge, at which point the Hellish beasts shot into the air in a 'flaught o fire,' proving the sacredness of running water.

YOUNG ROBIN AND THE FAIRIES

On another occasion Robin had fastened his horse to his cart and gone to Glasgow to purchase a barrel of ale. As he approached a place on the road known as Camore, he heard the sound of music and merriment. The place had a reputation as being the haunt of fairies, and, sure enough, when he reached the actual spot, he noticed all about him small people all dressed in green finery. While Robin was fascinated and even enchanted, the horse, on the other hand was spooked. Without warning it took off, throwing Robin in among the Guid Folk. His collision with the ground brought him to his senses and he raced homeward in the wake of the galloping horse. A mile down the road he found pieces of broken wheel and, finally, the poor beast dragging an empty wheel-less cart. In fear he retraced the road back a hundred yards where he found the barrel some yards off the road. Unfortunately, it had hit an erratic boulder and been staved in. The contents had leaked into the heather and peat, to the delight and inebriation of the Guid Folk.

It was weeks before Robin ventured out of doors after dark.

Glossary

A wee: a little while
A: I
Aa: all
Aamichtie: The Allmighty/God
Ablow: below
Abune: above
Acause: because
Ae: one
Aff: off
Aft: often
Aheid; ahead
Ahint: behind
Aiblins: perhaps
Aicht; eight
Ailsey: Ailsa Craig
Aiple; apple
Airn: iron
Airt: direction
An: and
Antrin; odd/unusual/strange
Appen; open
Asse-hole: ash-pit in a fire
Ava; At all
Awa: away
Awfy; awful
Aye: yes
Aye; always
Ayont: beyond

Baccy; tobacco
Baith; both
Bawbee: coin worth six pence Scots or half a pence sterling
Bere caff: barley chaff or husk
Bere: barley
Besom: brush
Big: to build
Biggit: built
Birlinn: Scots/Norse longship
Bittie: small bit
Blawit: blow
Blawn; blown
Bluid; blood
Bluidy: bloody
Blythe: happy
Bocht; bought
Bonny: beautiful
Braid: broad
Braw: fine, elegant
Brig: bridge
Broonie: house elf
Brose: a dish of boiling water, oatmeal, salt and butter
Brunt:burnt
Buik: book
Buits: boots
Burd; bird
Buss; bush
Butt an ben: house with cowshed and single-room home adjoining
Bylin: boiling
Byre; cowshed

Cadger: peddlar
Cannae: cannot
Cant (Scottish): language of the Lowland traveller folk.
Cantyre: Mull of Kintyre
Caup; cup
Caustle; castle
Chap: knock
Chapman: door-to-door salesman
Chow: chew
Cinner; cinder
Claes: clothes
Claith: cloth
Clarty: mucky
Clashes: very wet place
Cluds: clouds
Cog: wooden bowl
Conceat: to like
Consumpt; consumption/intake
Coontin: counting
Cootikens: thigh length gaiters
Corbie; crow
Coupin; falling over
Cruives: fish traps
Cuidna; couldn't

Cuist; cast
Daes: does
Daith; death
Daurk: dark
Daurna; dare not
Daurksome: sad/melancholic
Deid; dead
Deid-kist: dead-box, coffin
Denner; dinner
Dern; dreary/desolate
Dizzen: dozen
Dochters; daughters
Dooble; double
Doon-heid: dislike
Doun: down
Doze; drowsy
Drappie; small drop
Dree ma weird: face my fate
Dreid; dread
Droonin; drowning
Drouth: thirst
Dug; dog
Duin' done
Dune: done
Dwam: dream/trance
Dyke; drystone wall

Eegit: idiot
Een even
Een: eyes
Eerie: fearful
Eneuch; enough
Erin: Ireland
Erse: bottom/backside
Erse; Irish
Esk: newt

Fae/frae: from
Fand: found
Fardel: quarter of a large round oatcake
Fash: worry
Faur: far
Faus: false
Fecht: fight
Fegs: an interjection from the word faith

Fer; for
Ferlie: a wonderful thing
Fermer; farmer
Fin: find
Flaught; flight
Flee: fly
Freenly: friendly
Fuit; foot

Gaird: guard
Gait; goat
Gallimaufrey: jumble of things
Gang: go
Gaun: going
Gear: goods/property
Geegaws: cheap jewellery
Gibbet; gallows for hanging people
Gibbous: when the moon is more than half
Gin: if
Glamourie: magic spells
Gomerel: fool
Gowd/goud: gold
Graith: equipment
Gran: grand
Gress; grass
Grimoire: books of magic spells
Grise; pig
Guddlin; catching fish by hand
Guid: good
Guidfolk: fairies/sith
Guidwife: farmer's wife
Guidwillt: goodwilled
Guising: dressing up for Halloween
Gyte; mad/demented

Hae: have
Haffets: temples of the head
Hairst: harvest
Haiver: talk nonsense
Hallan: inside porch
Hantle: large quantity
Harquebus: small calibre matchlock gun from the 1400s
Haud; hold
Hauf: half
Haun; hand
Haunle; handle
Heich: high
Heid: head
Hert: heart
Heugh: crag/ravine
Hippet: hopped
Hissel: himself
Hissel: hisself
Hoose: house
Hostelry; pub
Houeer: however
Hungert: hungry
Hunner: hundred
Hure: whore/person of ill repute

I; in
Ileit: oiled
Ilka: each
Ingle; open fire
Instead: instead

Jo: dear
Juist; just
Jyne: join

Kailyard: garden
Kebbuck; cheese

Ken; know
Kenspeckle; colourful
Ketch: two-masted sailing boat
Keuk: cook
Kina: kind of
Kintraside: countryside
Kirn; butter churn
Kist; chest
Knowe: mound, hillock
Kye: cows
Kye; cows
Kyloes: native of Kyle district of Ayrshire

Laddie: small boy
Lan: land
Lane: river that runs between two lochs
Lang: long
Langsyne: long ago
Lauchin; laughing
Lea: leave
Leeve; live
Len: lend
Lift: sky
Loom: haze
Lowe/low; flame/fire
Lue: love
Luik: look
Lum: chimney
Lunnon: London
Lyart; streaked with white

Maist; most
Makit: made
Malifec: evil/bad luck
Mash-tun: vessel for converting crushed grain into sugars ready for fermenting in the making of beer
Maument: moment
Maun: may
Mebbe: maybe
Meenister; minister
Meenit: minute
Melancholia: sadness
Mercat: market
Merk: part-silver coin worth 13-14 scots shillings; around £6.50 today
Mey; may
Micht: might
Mirk: dark
Miscreant: villain, wrongdoer
Morn (the morn): tomorrow
Morra: tomorrow
Mort-claith: dead-cloth, winding-sheet for wrapping the dead.
Muin: moon
Munt: mount
Mutchkin: three-quarters of a pint
Nae: no
Naebody; no one
Naig/nag: horse
Neer: never
Neer; never
Neist: next
Nicht; night
Nocht; nothing
Nou: now

Oan: on
Oer: over
Onding; downpour of rain
Onstead:
Oo: wool

Ootcam: outcome
Ower: over

Pairts: parts
Pey; pay
Pickle; an amount, usually small
Pit: put
Plaidie: a long, rectangular piece of cloth, often tartan, used as a cloak or blanket
Pootch: pouch/purse/pocket
Pou: pull
Pown; pound
Puddock; frog
Puir; poor

Quaich: shallow, two-handled, drinking cup

Ratton: rat
Raisit: raised
Richt; right
Robbit: robbed
Row't: rolled

Sae: so
Sairry: sorry
Sall: shall
Sauch; willow
Sauf; save
Saul: soul
Saunstane: sandstone
Sawn: sown (corn or barley)
Sax: six
Schuil: school
Scowther; roasting
Seicont; second
Shaw: small wood
Shaw; show
Shill: shell/remove husks from corn
Shouthers; shoulders
Sic: such
Siccar; sure
Sicht; sight
Siller: silver/money
Sindoon; sundown
Sith; Gaelic for fairy folk
Smaa; small
Sodger; soldier
Spaewife; woman who can forsee the future
Speir; ask
Spence: storeroom
Spleuchan: pouch
Spunkie: will of the wisp
Stane; stone
Staun: stand
Steerie: high spirits, causing a disturbance
Stertlin; startling
Stervin; starving
Stey: stay
Stowp/stoup; drinking vessel
Stramash: uproar/disturbance
Strynge: strange
Suid: should
Suin: soon
Sweir: swear

Tae: to
Tae: toe
Taen: taken
Tak: take
Tastit: tasted

Telt: told
Thole: endure, suffer
Thoom: thumb
Thresh; thrash
Ticht; tight
Trauchle; trudge/drag
Travois: two poled transport device that is dragged
Tuik: took
Twae: two

Unner: under
Usquebeatha; whisky

Vaudie:
Verra: very

Waa: wall
Wae; with
Wag; proceed/move on
Wanweirdit: ill-fated/unfortunate
Wark; work
Warld: world
Warlock; male witch
Wat; wet
Watter: water
Wean: child
Weel: well
Whaur: where
Wheen: a number of; usually many
Whilk: which
Whinbush; gorse
Whinstone/whunstane: igneous (volcanic) rock. So-called because of the sound it makes when hit by a hammer.
Whit: what
Whyles; sometimes
Wi: with
Woo: wool
Worts: liquid just before fermentation in the making of beer
Wuid: would

Yae: one
Ye: you
Yersel: yourself
Yill: ale
Yin: one
Yowe: ewe, sheep

Archive.org
Carnegie Library, Ayr
Chamber's Popular Rhymes of Scotland
Historical and Traditional Tales Connected with the South of Scotland: John Nicholson
Historical Tales and Legends of Ayrshire: William Robertson
History of Dumfries and Galloway: Herbert Maxwell
Memorables of Robin Cummell: John Service
One Hundred Modern Scottish Poets
Scottish Ballads: Robert Chambers
Robert Burns Centre Library, Kilmarnock
Tales and Traditions of Ayrshire and Galloway: Andrew Glass
Tales of Ayrshire: Anna Blair
The Compete Works of Robert Burns: James MacKay
The Scottish Journal of Topography, Antiquities, Traditions, Etc
Townhouse Library. Irvine
Unique Traditions Chiefly of the West and South of Scotland: John Gordon Barbour
Wikipedia

Above are some of the sources for the tales, but not always. Sometimes their bibliographies, introductions or notes gave clues where to locate an early source. Old Ayrshire newspapers often provided a brief reference that was enough to track down a tale.